Trust and Understanding

the person-centred approach to everyday care for people with special needs

Marlis Pörtner

PCCS BOOKS

Ross-on-Wye

PCCS BOOKS
Llangarron
Ross-on-Wye
Herefordshire
HR9 6PT
UK
Tel +44 (0)1989 77 07 07

Klett-Cotta
© 1996 J.G. Cotta'sche Buchhandlung Nachfolger GmbH
Stuttgart
For the English language translation:
© 2000 Marlis Pörtner

Trust and Understanding
the person-centred approach to everyday care for people with special
needs

ISBN 1 898059 27 6

Cover design by Denis Postle.
Printed by Redwood Books, Trowbridge, Wiltshire, UK

Contents

Acknowledgements

My deep gratitude goes to all those who in various ways contributed to this book: to the persons whom in these last fifteen years I had the privilege to work with — in consultation, supervision or psychotherapy — and who in inestimable ways helped me to broaden my horizons of understanding. They all had their part in that the ideas presented here could develop and take shape.

Sincere thanks to Sigrid Baumann, Ursula Friedrich, Harry Hulskers, Barbara Krietemeyer, Petr Ondracek, Rini Schenck, Maria Schmucki, Cécile Schwarz, Angela Turner, Allan Turner and Dion Van Werde for informative conversations related to the subject of this book and for kindly contributing examples from their own professional or personal experience.

My special thanks to Garry Prouty, who was the first person to encourage me to write this book and whose concepts for me were confirming as well as pointing the way ever since I began to work for people with special needs.

I feel gratefully obliged to my German publishers Klett-Cotta for publishing the original German book. I thank Elke Lambers for recommending it to PCCS Books and Alexandra Szigeti for helpful advice with the translation.

And last but not least I want to express my most sincere esteem and gratitude to Maggie Taylor Sanders and Pete Sanders for making my concepts available to English readers, and to particularly thank Maggie for her sensible and sensitive editing. PCCS Books' willingness to foster the mutuality of exchanging ideas and knowledge between the languages is exemplary and pioneering and deserves deep appreciation and respect.

Switzerland, July 2000.

1
Introduction

The idea for writing this book emerged from many years of consulting staff members of different communities and institutions, as well as from my therapeutic work with people with special needs. More and more I realised how much the person-centred approach has to offer in this field. Moreover, to my surprise, more than once I saw it happen that carers, without having a specific knowledge of the person-centred approach, intuitively developed ways to work which were quite close to its principles. It seemed as if the experience of getting stuck with what has been tried before, sometimes would lead quite naturally to ways which embrace trust and understanding and offer the other person more space to take their own initiatives and responsibilities. These promising approaches mark points where we can begin.

Using concrete examples, we shall see what it means to work in a person-centred way in different fields and according to different tasks and circumstances. Person-centred work in other fields is not the same as client-centred psychotherapy. To make this very clear was another motivation to write this book, as so many misunderstandings and misjudgements of the person-centred approach result from not paying sufficient attention to this differentiation.

This may be one of the reasons why a consistent person-centred attitude and a solid knowledge of its fundamentals are only very rarely the basis of work in a social institution. Yet the person-centred philosophy is highly suitable to meet the specific requirements of this field. Working on its principles is likely to:
• improve life quality for the people taken care of
• extend their frame of action
• facilitate the staff's work
• diminish negative effects of frequently changing staff
• counterbalance burn-out symptoms.

Therefore it might be useful to establish a concept which makes explicit what it actually means to work in a person-centred way, and to develop guidelines which help to implement it in everyday work for people with special needs or in need of care. The concept, though, is not restricted to just these areas. Its principles are as well suited to be adapted to other fields and to be modified according to other tasks and circumstances. However, in this book the fundamentals of person-centred work are illustrated mainly by examples from working with adults with special needs, not only because in this field I have the most experience, but also because I feel that with them it becomes particularly visible — like through a magnifying glass — what is essential when working with human beings. In addition some other examples from my consulting experience, or reported by colleagues, will demonstrate how the same principles work equally well in other fields. Names and some details have been changed, in order to respect the anonymity of the people described. The variety of examples is meant to encourage the reader's own considerations about how to work in a person-centred way in their own professional field.

The use of language in this book

I completely agree with and support every effort to avoid disparaging terms and use a language which respects human dignity and integrity of people with special needs and I fully understand their concern and sensitivity about being labelled in a derogatory way. Yet very frequently it is not the language itself which is disrespecting, but the attitude with which it is used. This attitude behind the words is perceived by people with special needs. As long as the attitude does not change, changing the words will have only very limited effects.

It goes without saying that we have to carefully pay attention not to use terms which in themselves are disparaging (like 'cripple' or 'idiot', which were used in past times). But what we see now is how one word after another is rejected as disrespectful and consequently the language gets impoverished to a point where it can no longer adequately express the complexity of the subject, but is reduced to simplifications which in no way do justice to people with special needs. The term 'people with special needs' is very helpful as a general expression, but not suitable in every specific context and sometimes linguistically not correct. 'Learning disabilities' is a very specific notion grasping only one part of the problem, but not covering the complexity we have to cope with. Although it is true that people with special needs, as a rule, have learning disabilities, there is on the other hand a large number of people with learning disabilities who don't have in any way the 'special needs' we are dealing with here. In German we have different words, but similar problems. The British author Valerie Sinason[1] in a very informative and relevant chapter 'Euphemisms and Abuse' describes these problems and their historical roots.

1 Sinason (1992)

It is necessary to look more carefully at the real meaning of the words we use, in order to make sure that they are not disparaging and at the same time suitable to express the complexitiy of the issue we are talking about. Looking at *Webster's Collegiate Dictionary*, for example, we find the following definitions: 'retardation: . . . 3. slowness of development or progress'; 'handicap: . . . Figuratively, any disadvantage that renders success more difficult'; 'disabled: incapable; incapacitated.' It might come as a surprise that the most accepted term 'disabled' is actually the most limited and judgemental, opening no perspective, whereas 'handicapped' does not refer to the person herself but to the difficulties she has to cope with, thus describing the nature of the problem instead of labelling the person. Interestingly enough, the most disapproved term 'retarded' is, in its true sense, the most open-minded in terms of possible development and growth, as 'slow' in no way implies that development has stopped or is impossible. However, all these words might become disparaging when used with a derogatory attitude. As long as persons who are 'different' and who do not quite fit into what society considers 'normal' are met with disrespect and contempt, whatever name they are called will sooner or later be considered disparaging. If we keep in mind that to be handicapped, disabled, retarded, confused or demented etc., is not shameful, but a human condition, and that we have to accept and respect human beings suffering from these conditions, we are free again to use language appropriately and in a more differentiated way.

Therefore, as much as I am prepared to conform wherever possible with what is in common use, I shall now and then, where it is necessary to be more clear and explicit in what I have to say, take the liberty to use a term which might so far have been considered as 'not politically correct'. I do hope that for the readers the attitude of acceptance and esteem in which this is done will come through.

The male and female form for carers as well as for those they care for is used alternately.

2
Creating living spaces

Regardless of the difference in tasks of, for example, a nursing home, a community for people with special needs and an institution for adolescents with behaviour disorders, some fundamental considerations are applicable to any of the settings mentioned in this book.

Generally speaking, this book is about how to create living spaces for human beings who, for very different reasons, are not, not yet or not at all in a position to live independently. Such spaces must offer conditions which meet the specific needs of the people concerned and support as much as possible their capacities, their independence and their taking responsibilities for themselves. It is widely acknowledged that this is not just an issue of housing and feeding people, but a demanding and complex task which requires professional training and experience.

This certainly is an encouraging development, but there is also a 'dark side' to it. Together with the professional upgrading, ambitions grow. Carers define goals, try out methods and aim for changes, which sometimes correspond more to their own ambitions than to the needs of those they care for. Knowledge is useful, as it provides instruments to help other people to develop their abilities. But it may also result in a temptation to 'educate' other people. This is inappropriate with adults, and can be an arrogance which they usually refuse to accept.

Adults with special needs, even though their level of development may in some ways be comparable to that of a child, have lived lives too. Their years of experience cannot just be dismissed. Older people too, even though they may be weak, ill or disturbed, have lived their lives, the formative influence of which is still there. This we have to respect, as bizarre, childish or unrealistic as their behaviour may appear.

Adolescents are no longer children either, and they often refuse to be educated by others. And those considered to have 'behaviour disorders' usually have a long history of inadequate or failed education, which is unlikely to let them remain open for later catching up. Instead of trying to impose our educational ideas on them, we have to find other ways to facilitate their further growth, to encourage and support their taking responsibilities for themselves.

It goes without saying that trying to 'educate' people in hospitals or nursing homes or communities for the elderly is totally inappropriate. But attempts to educate sneak in here too. Carers sometimes have a very precise idea about what is right for the people they take care of, and — with more or less energy — try to impose it on them.

To know about diagnostics is helpful, and sometimes even essential, to understand better the 'otherness' of others. But it could also inhibit a carer seeing the other person's abilities and entice him to look at reactions and behaviour exclusively from the viewpoint of symptomatology.

To be consciously aware of this 'dark side' makes it easier to avoid its dangers. This in no way implies that professional skills and knowledge are unnecessary, or that it is enough to rely on common sense and experience or to adopt an attitude of 'laissez-faire'. On the contrary, we need our knowledge to understand better the people we take care of, and we have to use our skills to support them in a way that meets their different personalities and needs. It makes a crucial difference if we view knowledge as a way of deepening our capacity to understand and enabling the other person to make her own decisions instead of using it as an irrefutable instrument to classify and determine other people.

Working in a person-centred way . . .
. . . means *not starting from ideas about how human beings should be, but from how they are and from their potential.* It means taking the other person seriously in her own individual way, attempting to understand her ways of expressing herself, and supporting her to find, within her limited possibilities, her own way to adequately cope with reality.

This attitude does not just apply to individuals. It is helpful also in dealing with a group, a team or a community. Working in a person-centred way means solving problems, developing programmes and taking decisions together *with* the people concerned, not *for* them. It means considering and respecting their different abilities, needs and opinions and, within their possibilities, allowing them to take responsibilities for themselves. To work in a person-centred way means to be aware of and encourage the resources of an organism — be this an individual or a community.

A person-centred attitude applies as well to the carers themselves. They should learn to trust in their individual ways, their personal resources and abilities, and contribute them to their work. To work in a person-centred way means *to be transparent as a person.* This also requires that carers are willing to take into account their own part in a situation.

To work in a person-centred way also means to clearly acknowledge the frame of reference of a situation and of the people involved. On the one hand there is the structure of the institution or community — its financial and organisational conditions, the responsibilities of the staff etc. — which has to be considered and made transparent for everybody involved. On the other hand, in some areas and situations, it may be necessary to set a structure that enables the other person to release resources and develop capabilities. How this structure has to be designed, in order not to restrict a person but to define a safe space for self-determination, will differ according to different fields, different tasks and individual circumstances. To recognise the appropriate structure, and offer it to the other person, is a crucial aspect of person-centred work.

The concept presented here is aimed at providing orientation for the carers and supporting them in terms of how to cope with the standards described above in their everyday work.

Why a do we need a concept?

Is the professional training and competence of social workers, carers, nurses and teachers for special education not sufficient? Perhaps another concept — or concepts in general — inhibit spontaneous reactions and restrict individual ways of working? Surely a concept results in working mechanically along a rigid pattern, instead of being open to react to the particular situation?

If a concept has this effect, it is either not suitable or not properly applied. To work with a concept does not imply constantly staring at it and considering at each step if it does or does not conform. Most of the time we react spontaneously, and it cannot be the purpose of a concept to prevent spontaneity. But having a concept in the back of our minds extends the radius of our spontaneity, and at the same time defines its frame. A concept represents a frame of reference which:
• defines goals, fundamentals and priorities of our work
• settles a binding general outline and at the same time defines the open space for the staff's individual ways and initiatives
• offers a structure with which carers can compare their actions
• serves as a guideline when doubts arise or situations become critical
• offers criteria to compare differing opinions and clarify disagreements.

Moreover, a concept facilitates an effective staff policy. When hiring new carers, it allows us to:
• compare mutual expectations and ideas in a concrete way
• recognise differing opinions more quickly
• prevent wrong decisions and misunderstandings on both sides.

And it may to some extent prevent the people being cared for from being used as an experimental field for the staff to try out their different educational and philosophical ideas.

A concept grants continuity, not in a sense of dull routine, but a continuity of attitudes and conditions, which at the same time offers space for individual ways and is open to further development and necessary change. This kind of continuity can considerably improve the climate and the ways of living together in an institution or a community. Work will get less frustrating for the staff and become more relaxed as well as more interesting if it is informed by a concept which on the one hand offers clear guidelines and on the other requires initiative, creativity and alert attention for the different personalities of those in care. They will feel better and more secure if they can rely on the continuity of some basic conditions.

The following two examples, both concerning adult women with special needs, will help to introduce the subject and illustrate the idea.

Example 1

Gertrud is constantly hurting herself by picking bits of skin off her hands. For years the staff of the institution she lives in have tried in vain to stop her doing that. She rubs her bleeding hands on the walls, which are bloodstained wherever she goes. This absorbs her so much that she is hardly able to participate in the activities of the group. One day the staff decide to give up trying to stop her. Gertrud is now allowed to pick the skin off her hands, but under certain conditions: she has to decide if she wants to stay with the others and participate in their activities, or if she wants to pick her skin. If she decides to do that, she can do it on the sofa in the corner. If she wants to join the group activities at the big table, she has to stop it. The result is amazing: Gertrud still picks the skin off her hands, but considerably less now. The walls are not bloodstained any more. Her hands are less sore. In the morning, before the group activities start, she sometimes mumbles: 'Must decide, must decide,' and she always keeps the agreement not to pick the skin off her hands, as long as she participates in the activities of the group.

Example 2

Eva does not like housework. She complains violently whenever she has to do it. Everybody knows that and tries to calm her down. She continues to scream about the vacuum cleaner. One day, a staff member examines it more carefully and discovers that indeed there is a loose switch, which has to be held down with one finger in a very uncomfortable way. It is easy to get this switch fixed. And this way the staff members are in a better position to deal with Eva's resistance to participate in the housework as it happens instead of interpreting a technical problem as 'resistance'.

At first, Gertrud and Eva were met with a 'diagnostic' and 'educational' attitude. The staff knew their deficiencies and, out of experience and knowledge, considered themselves able to interpret the behaviours of the two women. In vain they tried to change the 'undesirable behaviours' which, on the contrary, increased and escalated into power fights with the staff. The successful solutions show a different attitude. The carers no longer worked from the assumption that they knew better what was right for the two women, but took them seriously and let them participate in the search for new ways. Instead of destructive power fights, constructive solutions were found with both of them.

Instead of trying to stop Gertrud's inappropriate behaviour, she was given space to take her own decisions as well as a structure which helped her change her behaviour. Eva's protestations were no longer dismissed as her usual well-known reaction to something she did not like. The staff took it seriously and tried to find out what it really was about. And as it turned out, Eva's perception had been quite realistic and there was a concrete reason for her complaining.

The two examples are different, and concern two quite different personalities. Gertrud showed a severely disturbed behaviour which did not only strongly affect herself, but also the people around her. With Eva, it was a simple, everyday situation which had no big impact, but nevertheless caused unnecessary tension and bad feelings. Gertrud is a severely disabled woman who barely talks. She has lived for years in this institution, where she participates in a special day programme for those who are not able to work in a sheltered workshop. Eva, however, is only mildly disabled and well able to express herself verbally. She lives in a small flat-sharing community for people with special needs and works in a sheltered workshop.

A side effect, perhaps even more important than the resolution of the problem itself, was that the women's self-confidence had been reinforced, as they experienced themselves as being able to move and change things. And the staff learned that they could trust people with special needs much more than they had imagined.

To meet human beings — however disabled, 'difficult' or 'maladapted' they may be — with the conviction that *for them* their strange and unintelligible behaviour *makes sense*, and to try to understand it, makes a crucial difference from just dismissing it as 'disturbed' and trying to control or stop it.

In both cases this attitude of the staff had positive effects. They intuitively discovered ways which corresponded to person-centred fundamentals, though they did not explicitly know about them. The next chapter will look at these 'fundamentals'.

3
Fundamentals of person-centred work

The person-centred approach has been developed by the American psychologist Carl Rogers (1902–1987), the founder of client-centred psychotherapy. At the beginning of his professional career, working with juveniles with behaviour disorders, Rogers found that his extensive theoretical knowledge did not help him much to really understand his clients. Adolescents and their parents frequently did not really know what to do with his diagnosis and advice, however accurate is was. Rogers discovered that it was much more helpful to listen carefully to the other person, and he learned that changes were more likely to happen when he could grasp *the person's view* of what was going on. This insight motivated him to look for new ways in psychotherapy and to write his first book *Counseling and Psychotherapy,*[1] which received remarkable attention. From 1945 to 1957 at the University of Chicago Rogers had the opportunity to test in practice his ideas on psychotherapy as well as to teach them and to do research. Together with a group of motivated colleagues he founded the Chicago Counseling Center. In 1951 his standard work *Client-Centered Therapy*[2] was published. Very soon his thinking went beyond psychotherapy. He studied developmental aspects of the person[3] and after moving to California in 1963 tried to apply his concepts to fields other than psychotherapy (groups, schools, companies, institutions). This extended application of his ideas he called Person-Centred Approach.[4]

The person-centred approach in other fields is based on the same fundamentals as client-centred psychotherapy[5]. To understand what it means to work in a person-centred way in other fields it is vital to know these fundamentals. But it is equally indispensable to recognise clearly that in other fields they have to be realised in a different way than in psychotherapy. In the following, I shall first give a short summary

---

[1] Rogers (1942).

[2] Rogers (1951).

[3] Rogers (1961).

[4] Rogers (1969, 1970, 1977, 1980,1982).

[5] Those are described in detail in my book *Praxis der Gesprächspsychotherapie,* Pörtner (1994).

of basic theoretical fundamentals of the person-centred approach and then point to a few additional aspects that in my view are relevant when working with it. A basic essential is a humanistic image of human beings.

A humanistic 'conception of man'

This philosophical approach views each human being as an autonomous and worthwhile person. It respects the differences of individuals. No two people are alike, not even two with the same disability or the same disease. Each individual has her own way of coping with her life. A humanistic view starts from the assumption that every human being is basically working towards *growth* and *self-actualisation* and has his own personal resources to change and to solve problems. These resources may be disturbed or impaired for various reasons, which include developmental disorders, traumatic experiences, lack of encouragement, diseases and old age. But they must be discovered and fostered. On principle *not we, but the person herself knows what is best for her,* although she may not have or have lost access to this knowledge.

Each person has to be taken seriously in her own personal way of expressing herself, even if we cannot immediately understand it. For that person it makes sense, and we have to respect that. Not always do we succeed in decoding this sense. We have to accept that many times we cannot break through the wall and get to understand the inner world of persons with special needs or of confused elderly people. But to know that her behaviour *for her* makes sense, even though for us it remains concealed, implies an attitude which in itself has positive effects. To meet a person with the assumption that her behaviour for her has a meaning we do not understand makes us approach her differently, than if we dismiss her as 'disturbed', 'crazy', or 'maladjusted'. We must try to *'feel into' her perceptions and feelings* even if they are not easily intelligible. Just *trying* to understand will change the quality of the relationship. Meeting people this way means tracking down hidden resources and awakening dormant potential, or at least it helps to preserve and support existing abilities and thus prevent them from diminishing more and more. This attitude is one of the basic conditions of client-centred psychotherapy[6], and it is also a main condition for person-centred work in fields outside psychotherapy. But we always have to bear in mind the different context of different areas.

---

[6] Rogers (1957).

The three elements of the person-centred attitude

Empathy is the ability to perceive sensitively and accurately the other person's experiencing and feelings, to enter her frame of reference as if we were the other person, but at the same time never to forget that we are ourselves and not the other. Empathy does not mean identification. Empathic understanding does not aim to interpret or classify the other person; rather it is an attempt to enter her world as accurately as possible. The experience of being understood in itself encourages growth.

Unconditional positive regard means accepting the other person without judging her, just as she is at the moment, with all her difficulties and possibilities.

Congruence means being consciously aware of our own experiencing and feelings, and being able to discriminate it from what we perceive in the other person. Congruence means meeting the client as the person we are, and not hiding behind a professional mask. This implies that we should be open to and able to accept our own feelings, impulses and impressions, but not to throw them unfiltered at the other person. We must be able to discern, within the frame of our task, when it makes sense to share our feelings and when it does not. Congruence also implies that the general set-up of a situation must be clear and transparent for all persons concerned.

The theory of self-concept[7] . . .

. . . allows a deeper understanding of what congruence means. It also helps to understand better the guidelines for person-centred work outlined in the next chapter.

The notion self-concept embraces the image a person has of herself and how she values this image. The self-concept develops on the one hand out of the immediate experience of the child (for example hunger-satisfaction) and on the other hand out of the values which are communicated to the child by the world around him (for example: 'If I get dirty, I am bad'). The self-concept is not fixed, but permanently developing and changing through the experiences a person makes along her life.

Obstructions and emotional difficulties arise when experiences, feelings and sensations cannot be accepted, because they do not conform to the self-concept. In other words, the self-concept can be fixed by rigid

---

[7] Rogers (1951).

external values or taboos (e.g. 'Getting angry is bad').

Congruence exists when *the self-concept conforms to experience.* The self-concept is flexible and able to accept and integrate new experience.

Incongruence exists when *a rigid self-concept* cannot allow new experiences, feelings or perceptions, unless they conform to the existing narrow limits. The others have to be denied, suppressed, rationalised, reinterpreted, or may not even be perceived.

As mentioned before, there are a few more crucial aspects to be considered in the practice of the person-cented approach. I shall particularly specify those which are relevant for the professional fields we are dealing with here.

The balance between structure and freedom
It is very important to carefully acknowledge the structure of a situation. A carer has to be clearly aware of where her empathy is directed in this particular situation. She should recognise where the boundaries are that she needs to respect, as well as where she has herself to define boundaries or to make demands. To neglect this frequently leads to misunderstandings and deceptions.

An everyday situation is different from a therapeutic situation. The frame of psychotherapy is the therapy session. Its central issue is the client's experiencing and the therapist's aiming to understand it as accurately as possible. The structure of a community is different. It requires that carers not only empathically understand those in their care, but also acknowledge the circumstances of the community. A simple example may illustrate this.

Example 3
John lives in a small flat-sharing community for people with special needs. He does not like to participate in the housework. Yet the people live in this community on condition that the house is basically kept by themselves. Every time John has to do the dishes, he complains vehemently, before finally he does them reluctantly and with much grumbling. How can the social worker in this situation be empathic and accepting? Not, of course, by doing the dishes herself, nor by getting somebody else do them, but by understanding and accepting John's anger and irritation, and by communicating this to him (for example: 'You are angry right now, because you have to do the dishes', 'You don't like to do the dishes.').

Thus John's feelings are empathically understood and his irritation accepted. But in terms of his duties the limits are clear; he has to do the dishes. This is a crucial distinction: on the one hand the carer has to *empathically understand and accept the emotional reaction of the other person*, but on the other hand she has to *respect and represent the structure of the community*. Some carers have difficulties accepting structures and tend to blur them. However, many actions — especially of adolescents — are aimed precisely at getting the boundaries clearly set, which silently are there anyway.

The boundaries are defined on the one hand by the structure of the community and by the specific circumstances of the particular situation, and on the other hand by the resources and limitations of the staff, and the resources and limitations of the clients. It is crucial to acknowledge and take into consideration these boundaries, because only in this way can we recognise the space within which the person-centred attitude can work.

The balance between structure and freedom is a crucial factor in this work. It is relevant at various levels and in different contexts. Both structure *and* freedom are needed: they are interdependent, complementary and have to be maintained in an appropriate balance for the situation, and for the people concerned. To keep on finding and maintaining this balance is an essential task for professionals in this field — be it working with people with special needs, or people in need of care or showing behavioural disorders. To offer the best possible conditions to live and develop always implies giving *as much structure as needed and as much freedom as possible*. Quite often only one is acknowledged and the other neglected.

In earlier years — and this has still some influence today — special education for people with special needs emphasised structure. It is true that structure is necessary. Yet if structure does not, at the same time, include space for a person's own decisions and initiatives, it will inhibit, more than promote, her growth. However, it does not help a person with special needs if we just aim at giving her freedom to make decisions, without attention to a helpful structure. If the space is not protected by defined boundaries, if it is too wide and open for her to survey, she will get stressed and be unable to use it. It needs a structure to make the space visible. It needs leeway to make sure that the structure does not just restrict people, but defines a safe place where they are encouraged to try out their own impulses and take their own decisions.

Example 4

Hanna collects everything. Her room is stuffed with dolls, knick-knacks, old papers, empty boxes, etc.; she cannot throw anything away. Once in a while, when her room brims over, the social worker has a hard time trying to persuade Hanna that it needs to be tidied up. She does not want to sort out anything that she has accumulated. The social worker is reluctant to just tell Hanna what she has to do, or to tidy up the room herself. He would like to leave it to Hanna. But when he tells her that some time she will have to tidy up her room, nothing happens. He has an idea: he sets a time limit within which the room has to be tidied up. Hanna can choose if she wants to do it by herself or with the social worker helping. It is also (within the set time limit) up to her when she will do it. As she is not able to give an immediate answer, he writes the different options on a sheet which he sticks to the wall and asks Hanna to mark her choice with an X. When the carer comes in the next day, Hanna has marked, 'Wednesday; together with social worker'.

This is a simple example of what it means to find an adequate balance between structure and freedom. Out of consideration for the room-mates as well as for hygiene reasons, Hanna cannot be excused from tidying her room. She *has to do it* — this is the structure. But within that structure Hanna has *a choice between different options* — this is the freedom.

Such minimal choices may seem unimportant to outsiders. For Hanna — and not only for her, but for anybody whose life is largely determined by others — any space for her own decisions is significant, however small it might be. To have options has an influence on life quality. To be allowed to take decisions means to be taken seriously and treated as an adult person, it means to act independently — even though in a limited area. Human beings for whom everything is decided by others, and who have no choices at all, will become either rebellious or apathetic. The former results in weary power fights, the latter in resignation. Both ways are definitely not beneficial, whether for the person herself or for the people around her. Therefore her own decisions have not only to be respected, but stimulated and encouraged as much as possible.

To find an adequate balance between structure and freedom is a demanding task. It is not something static which can be discovered 'by diagnostics' and then fixed. It is a subtle balance, continuously to be watched and, if necessary, modified — not *for* the other person, but *together with* her. Carers must be attentively aware of changes and steps of growth. They have to carefully notice if and how the freedom is used, if it is too small or too large, and if perhaps the boundaries need to be altered.

Example 5

Herman cannot deal with his money. Every time he gets his salary at the workshop, he immediately spends it to the last penny at the shopping centre across the street. He already has accumulated hundreds of toy cars, and he continues to buy new ones. He then has no money left for other things. If for instance the group goes out for a coffee, one of them always has to pay for Herman. All attempts to persuade Herman that he should save money for such occasions and not spend it all on toy cars have failed. The very day Herman gets his salary, he compulsively spends it on toy cars. The social worker agrees with Herman to split the money into different envelopes, one for each week, and to take just one at a time, on the day indicated on the envelope. It works. Herman seems even to appreciate this support, and he keeps the agreement. Yet it is important for Herman to know that on the day of payment when he comes home, the social worker will be there and, together with him, prepare the envelopes.

In this example a narrower structure was helpful for Herman, as he could not handle the complete freedom to budget his money himself. He even felt relieved to get this support. Yet he still had some independence, because nobody controlled when he would take the envelopes with the money from the drawer. It remained his own responsibility to keep to the agreement.

Sensitivity to recognise individual possibilities and limitations, openness for changes and flexibility to react to them are required. But equally important is clarity about what is fixed and therefore cannot be negotiated.

Clarity . . .
. . . is something which may not naturally be connected with the person-centred approach, and indeed is often neglected. However, clarity is an indispensable condition for the person-centred attitude to work. Lack of clarity leads to the misunderstanding that empathic understanding and acceptance are just a vague 'being nice' and 'laissez-faire' attitude. Staff, wishing to be democratic, frequently tend to not acknowledge facts — especially unpleasant ones — or to blur them, even for themselves. Thus they ignore the need for congruence, which for the person-centred attitude is at least as important as the two other elements. Congruence also implies clarity about the boundaries within which decisions are possible, and about facts that cannot be changed.

Many people working in social professions have a hard time providing this clarity. They tend to discuss everything, even matters on which the other person finally has no influence at all. Yet there is nothing more disappointing than the illusion of having a choice when there is none. Certainly staff members do not always deliberately create such illusions. Often only after discussing it with the other person, do they realise that in fact the decision has already been made.

Example 6

A small community for people with special needs is to admit a new member. Two people have applied. Both are invited for a visit. Afterwards the staff discuss with the group whom they would choose. The group expresses a clear preference. Only later staff and management realise that, for reasons the residents could neither know nor judge, this young man cannot be accepted and they decide on the other applicant. It is quite understandable that the residents are irritated and complain about their choice not having been acknowledged and about the staff first asking them, but then still making the decision over their heads.

Management and staff definitely should have verified if there was a real choice for the group, before discussing it with them. It would have spared these people with special needs another experience of being disappointed and not taken seriously. Such experiences do not reinforce trust, but leave people feeling discouraged. A little more reflection could help to avoid that.

Confusion coming out of thoughtlessness does not just happen for people with special needs. I remember an example from a regular primary school.

Example 7

In a second grade class a new teacher is to temporarily replace the current teacher who will be on leave for six months. Several applying teachers give test lessons. After that, the regular teacher discusses with the class the different applicants and whom they liked more and whom less. The children take this very seriously, as they believe that their opinion will be taken into consideration for the selection. The teacher who is finally hired is the one they liked the least.

It is easy to figure out the dreadful effect this had on the children's trust in adults. And it was not helpful for the new teacher either. He had a very difficult start, and failure was predictable. The general situation — that the new teacher was to be selected by a board, on which neither the current teacher nor the opinion of the children had any influence — had neither been taken into account, nor made transparent. To discuss the matter with the children just raised futile expectations, which afterwards were disappointed. A sensible way to let the children participate would have been to tell them which teacher had been selected, and then to talk with them about their reactions, feelings and worries.

Carers are sometimes reluctant to give their clients clear information about something which has already been decided. They ask for their opinion, as if it would still have an influence, and at the same time try to make the taken decision sound appealing to them. In other words, they try to manipulate them towards where they want them to go. People with special needs are relatively easy to manipulate. To avoid that is an other reason why clarity is necessary. Fairness requires informing people clearly about given facts, and then accepting that the other person may not be pleased. Here again we need to be empathic and take the experience of the other person seriously. We have to acknowledge and accept her feeling of disappointment, anger, irritation or sadness.

Experience as an essential factor

How something is experienced is at least as important, and sometimes much more so, than *what* has happened. Each person's experience is different. What may terribly upset or scare one person does not bother the other. What somebody may experience as intrusive may be helpful for somebody else. What for one person is a pleasure, is a burden for the other. Experience is subjective.

The subjective experience is a central aspect of the personality, a key for understanding and an access to resources. This still is not sufficiently taken into account. We tend to take our knowledge, our norms (and sometimes also our own subjective experience!) as an objective standard — although the other person cannot relate to it, because it does not conform to the way she is experiencing. A carer tries to persuade a woman with a disability that the situation is really different from what she feels, instead of trying to understand how she experiences it, and to go from there to find a way. A nurse tells a patient what he has to do in order to feel better, instead of being interested in how he experiences and deals with his disease, and in the resources he could mobilise. Changes can only occur from a person's own experiencing, not from outside. To feel her experiences are understood can be of vital help for a person's ability to change. Therefore it is essential that carers are able to be empathic with the experiencing of the people they have to take care of.

Example 8

Roland, a man in his eighties, has been moved to a nursing home a few weeks ago. He is very confused and quite rebellious. He is incontinent and no longer able to wash himself. But he fiercely refuses to be washed by the nurse and turns away from her, so that she cannot reach him. The nurse tries to persuade him to turn around, but this only makes things worse. The more the nurse tries, the more violently Roland defends himself. The nurse gets more and more impatient, but then all at once she realises that an impasse has been reached. She relaxes for a second, takes a deep breath and tries to imagine how Roland might feel. Then she says: 'You feel embarrassed, Roland, because I have to wash you, which is why you turn away from me.' Roland turns around and docilely allows the nurse to wash him.

The example shows how helpful it can be, for both sides, when carers in difficult situations try to understand what their client is experiencing. It is not without reason that experience has such an important place in humanistic psychology. Recent approaches in nursing based on humanistic fundamentals (see Chapter 11) also view the subjective experience of the patient as an important factor that should be paid more attention to. Even in medicine the importance of subjective experience is increasingly acknowledged.

Change lies in personal resources, not deficiencies
Sometimes the limitations of a person are so much the focus of attention that what is there is hardly noticed. Thus abilities cannot grow, but will wither. Yet the potential for development and change does not lie in the deficiencies, but in the resources. These have to be discovered, encouraged and made use of. The 'diagnostic eye' which constantly looks at deficiencies tends to focus on what people with special needs — or the elderly or the ill or the maladapted — cannot do, blurring the view of what they still can do.

Older people tend to judge themselves — and to be judged — mainly by what they are no longer able to do or what has become worse. Thus new aspects that could emerge are overlooked. For example, confused older people whose thinking is impaired, sometimes develop new emotional and intuitive qualities.

Of course, we must not turn a blind eye to a person's limitations. But it is essential to realise that limitations can be considered from different viewpoints. Looking at limitations from the viewpoint of what is actually there is quite different from looking at them and seeing something missing. To start from what is there, implies that there is some potential for growth, and that perhaps the boundaries could be moved a little bit.

Example 9
John has to prepare a carrot salad. He bought two pounds of carrots and asks the social worker, 'Do I have to prepare them all?' The social worker shows him the other salads, already prepared, and asks him to guess how many carrots might be needed. 'I can't do

that' is John's clear statement. The social worker is disappointed that John seems not to be able to make any progress on that score.

This could be seen differently: I think it *is* a progress that John is so clearly aware of his limitations and asks for help. It shows that he copes with this problem in a realistic way. Instead of just noting John's lack of imagination, the carer should also pay attention to and encourage what is there: John's being realistic about his ability and knowing when he needs help. This is a resource which could be further developed and of use in other situations too. This example also demonstrates that very small steps sometimes bear the potential for further development.

Small steps . . .
. . . that are so easily overlooked are particularly meaningful. Each step, as small as it may be, proves that a person is able to move forward, and carries the potential for further steps. Therefore carers should meticulously look for these small steps — with a magnifying glass so to speak — and welcome them wherever they detect them.

Steps of growth can only be integrated, if a person is allowed to take them *at her own pace*. This is particularly true for people with special needs. In a life widely determined by the pace of 'normal' people, they permanently experience being overtaken and falling behind. Some of them, especially the mildly disabled, develop considerable skills to hide this. The carers sometimes do not even notice it and this causes further stress. The experience of being inadequate and unable to follow is so omnipresent and overwhelming for most people with special needs that they hardly notice the small steps they do achieve here and there.

This too is not only true for those with special needs. A great many people are much more clearly aware of what they did not (or not yet) achieve, than of the steps they did achieve, and therefore feel depressed and hopeless. It is worth sharpening our eyes for these small steps. Each step gives rise to hope and courage even if it leads — as we could see in the previous example — in a different direction from the one the carers had expected.

The road is as important as the destination
The crux in defining so-called educational or behavioural goals for a person with special needs is that success is defined in terms of achieving the goal. Eyes are so fixed on the goal that what happens on the way is overlooked. Impulses pointing in another direction are not attended to, although they might open up new perspectives, if only the carers do

not stick so closely to their defined goal. For a person with special needs, the experience of being on the road, able to move and change something, is sometimes much more important than arriving at a specific destination or solving a particular problem. The person no longer experiences herself as blocked, but as being on the move. This must be noticed and encouraged by the staff.

Example 10

In an adult continuing education programme, people with special needs learn how to express their concerns. Paul had always wished to have a single room, but never dared to say so. In a role-play, he has the opportunity to try out how he could express his concern to those in charge in his institution. The next evening at the programme, he happily tells the group, 'Have said it' and 'Lottery'. As this institution provides only a limited number of single rooms, and several people are applying, the staff has decided to do a lottery the next time a single room is available. And Paul is lucky: he wins the single room ticket. This happens just before the summer break. After that a new programme starts, in which again Paul participates. The facilitator asks him how he is doing in his single room. Paul says, 'No single room anymore. Much too boring.'

In this case priority had not been given to the goal, but to the road Paul covered. His wishes had been taken seriously. He was allowed to make his own experiences, and afterwards to change his mind. Although the staff felt they could have told Paul in advance that he would not like the single room, they let him, step by step, experience this process himself, and accepted what he decided upon. It is quite obvious that such an experience is much more rewarding for a person than a decision made by others 'for his own good'.

This *process-oriented view* which acknowledges and accepts changes, rather than sticking to what was known before, is characteristic of person-centred work, which aims to encourage a person's personal growth.

Trusting the potential for growth

This, at first sight, may seem to be a strange principle, only justified perhaps when working with adolescents, where the task actually is to foster growth. But isn't this trust out of place in the group of people we are dealing with here? Is growth still possible at all with older, or even confused, people in need of care? Did not their development stop, or is it even declining? Should ill persons not just recover or, if this is not possible any more, accept their disease? What has this to do with growth? And being a person with special needs, does this not imply that at some point no more growth is possible? Isn't it the carers' task, at this point, to help out and give support? How should they trust the potential of growth?

As long as they live, human beings have again and again to confront and cope with changing circumstances. Restrictions also represent changes and require a different perspective. Changes may concern the environment, a new carer, a different room, a new room-mate etc.; or the person herself, her aches and pains, losing her sense of orientation etc. A disease too may imply new perception and growth, as it requires modifications of self-image, attitudes or way of life, in order to cope with and feel as comfortable as possible in the new situation.

Often lifetime habits no longer conform to changed circumstances. They have to be given up and new ones found. This also means growth. In this way, even with older, confused people, or those with a disability, there is still growth, as, within the realm of their possibilities, they have to cope with new situations. If we start from the assumption that an organism basically is aimed at realising resources to optimally adapt to new circumstances, it seems not too much out of place to trust the potential for growth and to encourage it as much as possible.

With adolescents it goes without saying that we have to trust their potential to develop. However, adolescents who are considered neglected or having behaviour disorders frequently are given alarmingly poor opportunities. Much too often it is by restricting measures that carers try to stop undesired behaviour and to enforce specific changes, whereas they should provide an adequate structure and enough freedom for the young person to take her own steps of development.

Are adults with special needs in any position to modify the rigid behaviour patterns marked in their childhood? Are older people still able to let go of cherished habits and principles, and develop new ways? It seems realistic not to expect too much, but to remain open to surprises. It is sometimes amazing the unexpected steps a person suddenly takes, which nobody would have believed them capable of.

Example 11
Bernard, a 37-year old man with severely impaired hearing, not able to talk and with strongly autistic features, when having a meal with his family, as soon as he had finished eating, used to get up and settle down in his favourite chair in the other room, whilst the others still sat together and talked. Only recently, for the first time, he came back after a while and sat with the others at the table until everybody got up. And also not long ago, he who all his life had avoided touching, for the first time laid his hand upon his mother's hand and left it there for a while. His family remained speechless;

all at once Bernard showed behaviours they never before had seen. Obviously Bernard is not just stuck in his emotional development.

A person-centred attitude implies basically trusting in a person's potential to grow, but — and this is equally essential — does not force growth. *Only when a person is accepted just as she is does change become possible.* But a time of stasis may also make sense and be a necessary breather to enable a person to take the next step.

If no further development is possible, it is an important task for the carers *not to reinforce rigid patterns or reduce even more the limited opportunity for growth.* Frequently carers do not see , or underestimate, this demanding aspect which not only requires an attitude that does not ignore the potential for growth, but also does not force change.

Personal responsibility
The person-centred approach highly values personal responsibility. It believes that each and every person, regardless of their abilities, is capable of taking some responsibilities for themselves.

Personal responsibility is not an absolute notion. We cannot concede personal responsibility to a newborn baby. Learning to take more and more responsibilities in ever larger areas is an essential aspect of growing. To respect and encourage as much as possible the client's personal responsibility is a basic concern in person-centred work.

People in need of care have, of course, only limited opportunities to take responsibilities. Unfortunately this frequently results in taking all of them away. Yet there is always an area, as tiny and insignificant as it may appear, in which they *can* take personal responsibility. And in this area it *has* to be fostered. Carers, instead of thinking 'I know better' should discover such areas and encourage those they care for to take responsibility. For a severely disabled person, this could mean letting her decide herself if she wants the door open or closed. Or for another person, letting her choose if she wants to take the umbrella or get wet when going outside — something seemingly quite basic may represent an opportunity for the person to take responsibility for themselves. Why is this so important?

Taking responsibility implies being taken seriously and not being totally dependent on others. This has an influence on life quality and self-esteem. The more restricted the opportunities for a person taking responsibility for herself, the more important it is not to take it *completely* away from her. Otherwise her abilities to do so will more and more deteriorate and her dependence on others increase.

Example 12

After a stroke, Lore is paralysed and no longer able to speak. She lives in a nursing home. A friend is visiting who very sensitively relates to her, and whose presence Lore obviously enjoys. A nurse comes in to clear away the coffee tray. Suddenly he remembers that in the lobby a children's choir is giving a performance for the inhabitants of the nursing home. He takes the wheelchair, saying, 'Let's go, Lore, we have a performance out there!' and drives the flabbergasted Lore out of the room, without noticing the equally flabbergasted visitor, nor making sure if Lore is at all interested in the choir, or if she would prefer to stay in her room with her friend.

Unfortunately very often everyday life in institutions is determined by such ways of not acknowledging the residents' personal responsibilities. The nurse certainly meant well, as he did not want Lore to miss the special event. But 'meaning well' does not give anybody the right to ignore desires and personal responsibilities of people in need of care. This would result in increasing their dependence more and more, until in time they are no longer able to make a decision and take responsibility for it.

From the foundations described above, we can deduce some useful guidelines for everyday living and working.

4
Guidelines for everyday work

These guidelines offer an explanation of what is essential in person-centred work and what it emphasises in practice. The basic condition, however, for carers is to be genuinely interested in the people they have to take care of. *Without genuine interest in other human beings and in how each person is different and has her own idiosyncratic ways, these guidelines could not be practised in a meaningful way, but would remain just empty phrases.*

Listening . . .
. . . is *the basic* foundation of person-centred work: listening to a handicapped person who has difficulties expressing herself; listening to older people even if what they say sounds unrealistic and confused; listening to adolescents, however immature and weird their ideas may appear; listening for nuances, for clues of change, own impulses, needs or desires, for feelings and moods. Listening is essential to understanding how another person feels and what she needs, but also for the carer to find out how to respond to her. Without listening there is no satisfying caretaking or support. Carers have to listen before they can do anything or make necessary arrangements for the other person. And it means *to listen with all senses,* to reactions, feelings and sensations which are not verbally expressed.

This also means *looking* — not in the sense of 'observing the behaviour' of the other person in order to interpret and judge her, but in the sense of *entering her world and carefully paying attention to clues of her experiencing.* Does somebody appear tense or relaxed, does he look scared, or sad, or happy? Does she tend to come close, or does she prefer to withdraw? How does he react to what I do, what does he seem to like and to dislike?

Taking the other person seriously
Even if a person expresses herself in an unintelligible way and her behaviour appears bizarre, she should always be taken seriously. A nurse should take it seriously when a patient complains about pains, even if she thinks she knows from experience that such severe pains

are impossible in this case, or that the pain relief she gave the patient must have had its effects long since. The carer should take seriously what the old woman is saying, even when she finds it hard to believe.

Example 13

Alice, a woman of eighty-two, lives in a nursing home. In talking with a Spanish-speaking employee, she recalls a trip to Argentina she had made when she was eighteen. She tells the nurse about the ocean-liner on which she had travelled, and about her uncle's estate where she had stayed. For the nurse this is an unknown world in which she does not believe. As Alice is confused sometimes, the nurse dismisses her account as pure fantasy. She is only half-listening, saying 'mm' from time to time. Alice is aware of it and gets upset. By chance Alice's daughter comes by. She knows about this trip to Argentina, which actually had represented a major event in her mother's life. The nurse is quite surprised and has a hard time accepting this, because it does not fit the idea of this confused old woman she had formed in her mind.

So the event Alice clearly remembered — despite her temporary confusion — had been absolutely real and meaningful for her life. To listen carefully to her and take her story seriously would have given the nurse useful insights into Alice's former life and the world she had lived in and could have opened new perspectives in how to respond to her.

However, usually it does not even matter if the facts are true or not. What is important is that for the other person it has meaning in the moment. *This* must be taken seriously. Perhaps it is just an image for a mood, a feeling, a desire or for whatever she may have in mind and cannot express differently. This showed also in the course of psychotherapy with the mentally disabled 20-year-old Catherine[1].

Example 14

Catherine, in nearly every session, fantasised about accidents and hospitals; she had to go to the hospital this morning and the ambulance came to pick her up, or the hospital had called, she should come and hold somebody's hand during his operation, etc. Though this was obviously not true, I took it seriously and responded to what she told me. After a while it turned out that these hospital fantasies were reminiscences of a traumatic experience she so far never had been able to process; at 15 she had been sterilised, without anybody preparing her for the operation or explaining to her what she would have to go through.

1 Pörtner (1990).

These examples make it very clear how essential it is to take seriously what a person tries to express, and not to dismiss it as a 'handicapped' or 'confused' person talking, even if we cannot understand or believe it. To try *to 'feel into' her subjective perception and frame of reference* does not only cause a person to feel better understood, it will also open new horizons of understanding for the carers, thus making their work more interesting and more alive.

Needs and desires too must be taken seriously, regardless of whether they can be met. Whether a desire is accepted, even though for some reason it cannot be fulfilled, or dismissed as improper, feels quite different. The example of little Cathy very nicely illustrates this difference.[2] However, we have often a hard time with this differentiation. We tend to identify accepting with granting, and to dismiss a desire or a need if we are not able to grant it. Could this also have something to do with our difficulty of accepting our own limits — in this case of not being able to meet the other person's needs?

To take a person seriously implies another principle which should go without saying, but actually is very often neglected: in the presence of a person with special needs *never talk about her, but always with her*. To talk about people as if they were not there, although they are present in the same room, is a bad habit quite common in institutions as well as in families. People do this not only with children, but also with adults, especially with the disabled or confused, thinking: 'They do not understand it anyway.' This is an error. People who cannot hear or are not able to express themselves, usually are very sensitively aware of others talking about them and of the mood in which it is done. The negative effect of this repeated experience of 'not being there' on self-esteem and a person's contact with reality is obvious.

Working from normality

To go from the normal situation for a person in our care reinforces the reality contact of disabled, confused or mentally ill persons. This, of course, does not mean overstressing them with demands that do not take account of their handicaps. Yet we should not qualify every 'difficult' behaviour as a 'special need', but ask ourselves if it could not just represent a personal peculiarity we easily would tolerate in a 'normal' person.

Example 15

Otto lives in a flat-sharing community for adults with special needs. The inhabitants take it in turns to do the housekeeping and prepare

---

2 See Chapter 10, p.90, 'A children's home in Germany'.

the meals. Otto is not able to make a salad dressing. The staff again and again tried to demonstrate and explain to him how to do it. But he does not get it and always takes the bottle with the ready-made dressing. The staff are disappointed that he is unable to learn such a simple thing.

A learning disability may well be the reason why Otto is not able to understand how to prepare a salad dressing. On the other hand, many 'normal' people think they cannot make a good dressing and prefer the ready-made variety, without therefore being regarded as disabled. We could also see it this way: Otto estimates realistically his ability to make a salad dressing, and taking the 'ready made' bottle is an adequate way of dealing with the situation.

In the example of Alice and her trip to Argentina, we have seen how quickly carers sometimes dismiss an older person's quite realistic statement as confused, as soon as it does not conform to what they are used to. With psychiatric patients there is also the danger of seeing any unusual way of behaviour as a symptom.

Example 16

Helga, after a suicide attempt, is admitted to a psychiatric hospital. After getting over the acute crisis, she wants to hire, at her own expense, a private teacher to give her Arabic lessons during her stay — something the structure of this private clinic would certainly allow. However, the ward staff regards this as weird, as a clue for her loss of reality contact, even as a psychotic symptom. The patient's desire is not met. Instead, she is told to participate in the activities the ward provides to reinforce the patient's reality contact. What doctors and nurses do not know (and what they easily could have learned by talking with her) is that Helga is planning to start a degree in Romance languages, and Arabic is, if not an essential, a very useful foundation for a deeper understanding of Romance languages. From this aspect, Helga's desire was not weird at all.

Within the *context of her life,* Helga's wish to take Arabic lessons had more reality contact than the activities the ward provides. This had not been acknowledged and thus a chance to support *the patient's contact with the reality of her own life* had been missed.

Of course, it is impossible for carers to know everything about the life context of their clients. But that's exactly why they should not treat as a symptom anything they do not understand. For the time being they should work with the situation as they find it and take the other person's concern seriously. The shortest way to find out, within the context of her life, whether this concern is realistic, is to empathically respond to her. This implies that carers should stay only with the obvious: the statements, behaviours and experiences of those in their care as they manifest themselves in the moment.

Staying with the obvious

We should avoid interpretations and explanations based on a person's disability or disorder. We should not deny, depreciate or reinterpret, thinking we know better, but first of all stay with the obvious, *exactly with what the other person tries to express*.

Example 17

A patient with a not-yet well-known syndrome is admitted to a hospital for several weeks of treatment. For many years he has studied everything he could get hold of about his disease, which is chronic and quite painful. However, for the staff his illness is relatively new. The patient has clear ideas about how he wishes to be treated. He brings along books and computer printouts concerning his treatment.

This gets on the nerves of the nurses. They complain that the patient is difficult, always wanting something else and ringing for the nurses ten times a day. The consultant first encourages them to fully express their annoyance, then he asks: 'How does the patient experience his disease, how has he integrated it into his everyday life?' The staff have no idea. Now one of the nurses is told to ask the patient about these issues and then inform the others. The conversation with the patient opens completely new perspectives. All at once the person behind the 'case' emerges and is taken seriously. This enables the team to organise the nursing services in a way that suits and helps the patient better, and on the other hand is much more satisfying for themselves.

This detour could have been avoided had the staff stayed with the obvious. The patient, with his books and treatment diagrams, signalled, 'I know a lot about my disease and would like to have a say in my treatment'. To take this concern seriously shows interest and to respond to it would have led very quickly to important questions for the planning of the treatment. How does the patient experience his disease, how does he deal with it, and what are his resources?

Example 2 (p.8) with Eva and the vacuum cleaner showed how important it is in living with people with special needs to stay with the obvious. With a 'normal' person it would go without saying that we first check if something is wrong with the vacuum cleaner before we assume that something is wrong with the person. It should be the same with somebody with special needs. Only when the obvious does not make any sense should we try to find out what could be the hidden meaning. And the best chance to approach this is to stay accurately and concretely with what the person is expressing and, together with her, go with it step by step. In this context there is another important principle.

Don't let your guide be what you already know

Carers should not think that they know how a person will react, even if they have seen it happen a hundred times. It is possible, at any time, that a person will act completely differently. We should be open to that and not stick to what we already know about a person. This showed clearly in Example 11, (p.22) of Bernard. Of course, in many situations, our knowledge about a person's history and way of life may be very helpful and useful (see Example 32, p.43). Yet carers should not use it to pin themselves — and the person they take care of — down to it, but *should always stay open to new and unknown aspects of her personality.*

Facilitating and responding to a person's experiencing

A person's subjective way of experiencing must be taken into account if we want to create adequate conditions for her well-being. Only by paying attention to how a person is experiencing are carers able to proceed in a sensible way. Does the older man in the nursing home appreciate it when the radio is turned on, or does he look annoyed? How is it for Laura to be washed by a male nurse? Does Dora like it when the carer passes her hand over her hair, or does she find it intrusive? Is Frank pleased when the nurse puts his wheelchair to the table where the others are sitting, or does he prefer to stay by himself and look out the window? Does Alice enjoy the sun shining on her bed, or is the bright light too strong for her eyes? Carers must be able to respond to that. Wherever possible, they should try to diminish what is experienced as unpleasant, and to develop what feels agreeable for a person.

It is not always possible to change an environment or situation to the way a person wishes, but at least it gives her relief to be able to express desires and worries and to be taken seriously by the carers.

Example 18

A visitor wants to take Dora for a walk. She finds Dora crying at the entrance of the nursing home. It turns out that Dora is scared when the others have an argument. She would like to run away and vanish. After that the nurses pay more attention to Dora as soon as it gets loud on the ward. They talk with her or take her aside. This way Dora feels less panicked.

Sometimes it is possible, without much effort, to change something that is experienced as bad, threatening, frightening or just unpleasant; this may be something very ordinary.

Example 19

Seventeen-year-old Oscar joined the community for juveniles with behaviour disorders recently. He refuses to take a shower. The social workers try to convince him, to force him — it is hopeless. He shirks whenever he can. It is a weary escalating fight. Finally, the consultant has an idea: the social workers should propose that Oscar takes a bath. That's what they do: they even offer him a bubble bath. Oscar is delighted, and from that moment his personal hygiene is not a problem anymore.

There is no objective reason why taking a shower should be unpleasant and taking a bath pleasant, it is just Oscar's subjective feeling. To take that into account and to allow him a bath from time to time instead of forcing him to take a shower, spared the staff and Oscar many a fruitless argument and considerably contributed to the good relations which could develop between them.

As much as possible human beings should be allowed *to make their own experiences.* This again not only, but particularly, applies to people with special needs. Very simple everyday things which frequently, without much thinking, are done for the other person spoil their chances of making an experience and learning from it. It is much more helpful, for example, to take somebody outside for a minute and let her feel herself if she would be too warm with the coat or too cold without it, than to just say: 'Today you need your warm coat'. The same is actually true with children.

Of course there are limits. There are situations where people with special needs have to be protected from bad experiences. But this is something which is over-emphasised rather than neglected. To protect a person with special needs from any bad experience also means preventing her from learning to confront her reality and making her miss chances for good experiences. It is very important, though, not to leave somebody alone with a bad experience, but to talk it over with her and to consider together what could be learned out of it.

To be aware of how a person experiences may also help to better understand so called 'undesired behaviours' and to eventually develop alternatives.

Example 20

Bernard — whom we met in Example 11 — for some time now, before going to bed in the evening, holds his hands endlessly under the running water. The carers have a hard time persuading him to stop it and turn the water off. He never does it by himself. Perhaps the carers should try to find out what meaning this behaviour might have for Bernard. Perhaps it is a pleasant sensation to feel the running water on his hands? Perhaps they could try to give him a bowl filled with water where he could play with his hands. Or perhaps a hourglass could help to limit his habit to an acceptable scale.

These are just two of many possible ideas for how to deal with this behaviour. Perhaps none will work and the carers will have to think again and try something completely different. Yet to try to understand and possibly change a behaviour by taking into account the other person's experiencing, in any case is much more useful than to make a fight out of it — which most of the time will be useless anyway. Even if it is not possible to obtain major change, trying to grasp the behaviour of the other person through her way of experiencing helps to understand her better. Last but not least, this way of proceeding is considerably more interesting and rewarding for the carers than the weary attempts at stopping undesired behaviour or persuading the other person that things are different from how she experiences them.

Example 21
Elvira and Fanny live in a home for elderly people. They like each other and often spend time together. One day Fanny loses her key. Elvira is terribly upset and feels guilty about this happening to her friend. Although she had not been there when it happened, she cannot calm down and repeats constantly, 'It's my fault that Elvira lost her key.' The carer tries to talk her out of that, but in vain. Elvira repeats it over and over again. Finally the carer tries it in a different way: 'You are sad because Fanny lost her key, right Elvira?'. Elvira nods and very soon calms down.

Instead of persisting with her attempts to persuade Elvira, the carer tried to understand what was going on in her mind. Elvira obviously felt understood and could now let go of her self-accusation. This is one of many examples showing that it is much more helpful to respond to another person's *experience* than to argue about facts. Older people, having moved to an institution, frequently say, 'I want to go home', and the answer usually is, 'Your home is here now'. Very often they get upset then and protest. A wearing discussion takes place, until one of the parties finally gives up. It would make much more sense to try to grasp the experience expressed in their words: 'You are homesick', or 'You often think of home', or 'You are not quite settled in here yet'.

Encouragement
In the course of their lives, people with special needs are discouraged

over and over again. There are so many things they would like to, but cannot do. They either lose confidence in themselves or overestimate their capabilities and get discouraged once more. Older people are often discouraged by the diminishing of their abilities and lose confidence even in what they still are able to do.

Of course, we cannot meet these feelings with cheap encouragement like, 'It is not as bad as all that.' But carers should carefully pay attention to any sign of hope or courage and support it. They should reinforce a person when she achieves something, however insignificant it may appear. Small steps should not perish in the daily routine, but must be noticed and encouraged.

This is equally true for adolescents who are considered as having behaviour disorders. Very rarely, in the course of their lives, have they been encouraged, but over and over again confronted with their failure. Their self-esteem is very low, even though they may superficially hide this behind unrealistic overestimation of themselves. It is much more rewarding to detect their qualities than to stick to and wear oneself out on their mistakes.

Example 22

Peter is a very difficult juvenile, cocooned into himself, and with very erratic behaviour. He barely answers, or if he does, it is in a very strange way. He steals and breaks the toy cars his friends have collected. At the institution for juveniles with behaviour disorders nobody knows what to do with him. He is not thought to be capable of anything, but considered as hopeless and barely fit for life. Yet one day an educator discovers his craft skills. He observes how Peter very skilfully fixes a toy car he has broken. The educator picks up the thread and asks: 'Would you like to help me fix something some time?'. From that moment, every time there is something to be fixed, Peter is called. He stays at the institution for five years, and when he leaves he finds a job as the operator of an excavator in a gravel pit. His behaviour is still quite difficult, but on his excavator he has a good chance of coping with his life.

For Peter it was a decisive step to discover that he was thought capable of something. In the perception of his carers his deficiencies faded into the background and they noticed more and more what was there: his craft skills and his interest for any kind of machines. This they tried to support and to encourage.

Fostering a person's own way

People whose life is to a high degree determined by others usually feel a strong need to have their own way. When there is not much leeway for this need, it sometimes manifests in a person's sticking stubbornly to something the staff considers a minor detail, but is extremely important for this person. People with special needs often only vaguely feel the desire for autonomy and express it through rebellious and strange behaviour, which for the carers is not understandable.

Example 23
Every morning it is a dreadful struggle for the staff to wake up Anna. She complains, refuses to leave her bed, does not come down for breakfast and has finally to be forced to get up. Particularly with new staff members whose insecurity she senses, she goes to extremes with this fight. I suggest trying an alarm clock — it works. Anna gets up without any problem and is at breakfast on time. Obviously the alarm clock makes her feel that she is getting up on her own initiative and not because a staff member urges her to do so.

I prefer to talk about 'a person's own way' rather than about autonomy because, although there is common agreement that we have 'to foster the autonomy' of people with special needs, carers often have a clear agenda as to what those in their care should do 'autonomously'. Educators talk about autonomy in terms of how to 'bring adolescents to it', and it is often not very clear if it is the development of the young person they have in mind, or rather their own comfort. In relation with older people too, 'autonomy' is predominantly a matter of specific chores they should carry out themselves. What *they* want is rarely asked. What is called 'autonomy' quite often — unintentionally and very subtly — changes into to the opposite and becomes patronising. Yet to act independently sometimes means *not* to do what the carers expect or want. It is one of the paradoxes in social professions, that these impulses must be backed up. They should not be considered as an offence, but welcomed as a sign of a person trying to find her own way. This has to be encouraged wherever possible.

For older people, to do it their own way may also mean for once to stay in bed all day. For somebody with special needs it may mean not participating at a group excursion. *Autonomy always implies taking our own responsibilities.* This should be granted to a person wherever possible, even if she then does not act the way the carer thinks right.

Example 24
Ursina, 96, lives in a nursing home. Her thinking has remained very clear and she is happy to be still able to walk. Nevertheless she sometimes expresses the wish to die soon. Sometimes she refuses to eat, because she just does not feel like eating. Regularly the nurses admonish her, 'If you don't eat, soon you will not be able to walk any more.' They know how important it is for Ursina to be able to walk, and hope that this way they will motivate her to eat. But there

are days when Ursina has a good appetite and enjoys her meal. There is no reason to patronise her and ignore the fact that on some days she does not feel like eating.

During puberty the need for independence and developing one's own ways is particularly strong. This is a basic difficulty in institutions for juveniles. In this period of growth adolescents have a hard time with fixed rules and the world of adults, and in addition they have to cope with the restricted structure of a school or institution. It is very understandable that adolescents at this age first of all just rebel against everything, no matter what it is. Sometimes they cannot even recognise where there is actually space for their own decision. They need time to come to terms with the structure; they have to explore its limits, perhaps even to kick against it and try out if it really is solid. Only then will they be in a position to recognise the freedom they still have. It would be vain and counterproductive to interpret this as weird behaviour, bad intention or defiance.

It is not always easy to find the right balance. On the one hand adolescents need clear limits; on the other hand it is necessary for their development to oppose the adults and find their own ways. Educators often have a hard time understanding rebellion as a necessary aspect of growth, appropriate for this age. They feel offended, as they expect the adolescents to recognise that they are being helped and that it is good for them. They find it hard to accept the fact that most adolescents do not like to live in an institution.

Often the urge for independence appears in an extreme hairstyle or a way of dressing which hardly conforms to the standards of the educators. Hair particularly plays an important part in an adolescent's sense of identity and belonging. They usually react very badly when adults try to interfere on this point. It does not make much sense when an educator gives an ultimatum, 'By then you will have a haircut' or, 'As long as your hair is green you will not go out'. But perhaps a compromise can be agreed upon, such as at least to wash their hair. Basically, however, their appearance should be left to the responsibility of the adolescents themselves. They will make their experiences with it, and it is up to them if and whom they want to please.

Sometimes, with people with behaviour disorders, behaviours which actually represent an individual choice are seen as a sign of decline, or with people with special needs as an expression of their disability. On that score the state of a room is an inexhaustible issue. Ideas about tidiness and what a room should look like widely differ individually — even among educators. This individual choice should also be conceded to residents of an institution, of course with respect to the limits of hygiene requirements. But within these limits, there has to be enough space to act individually. To foster a person's own way means also to offer clear and manageable choices.

Offering clear and manageable choices
It makes a difference for Frank's well-being in the old people's home if at breakfast he can choose his roll from the basket himself, or if somebody puts it on his plate; it makes a difference if he can choose the jam he has a liking for right now, or if he is just given one by the carer. It makes a difference for Alice if she has something to say about when she wants to have her nails cut, or if the nurses decide that without her. These details may seem irrelevant, but they have an impact on how a person, whose freedom anyway is very restricted, feels. Therefore they are worth more attention being paid to them.

Yet a lack of choices may assume quite other dimensions and have much more serious effects.

Example 25
In a home for juveniles with behaviour disorders it is obligatory to participate at the official Christmas dinner with the board, the minister, and with speeches etc. Most youths don't like this event. But they have only the choice to either participate or make their get-away with all the consequences this implies. Every year around Christmas several escapes take place.

To offer the young people some sensible alternatives from which they can choose — e.g. to organise the evening themselves in small groups or to have a celebration in the woods or whatever — would allow them solutions other than running away. To avoid escapes with all their negative consequences for the juveniles as well as for the whole community certainly is much more desirable than to have as many of them as possible, albeit unwillingly, participating at the official dinner.

Even for severely handicapped persons who can act independently only in a very limited way, sometimes tiny possibilities can be found to let them take their own decision, even, for example, to choose their coffee cup themselves. The more restricted a person's life, the more demanding the challenge for the carers to find out where they can offer her a tiny little bit of freedom for decisions. No matter how insignificant it may appear it is meaningful for the well-being of this person. On different levels and to a varying extent is it possible and necessary to offer choices. They improve life quality and reinforce self-esteem. Here too, an adequate balance between structure and self-determination has to be found. Choices have to offer real alternatives, yet they should not stress a person, but must *be clear and manageable for her* and adjusted to her individual capabilities.

Example 26
The carer in a small flat-sharing community for adults with special needs would like to motivate them not to spend every evening watching television, but to now and then turn to some other activity. All his attempts fail. If he asks the residents to make suggestions, how they could once in a while spend an evening differently, there is no response. Yet the social worker does not want to just organise a programme for them. A possible solution could be to agree with the group upon an evening when something else will be done, and to propose two or three concrete options from which they can choose.

In this example the social worker obviously expects too much of the people with special needs as the leeway is too large. They need a support to keep it within manageable limits. This leads to another important principle in caretaking: support for independence.

Offering support to act independently
Instead of just assuming that a person is not able to do something and to take over from her, it would make more sense to offer her support allowing her, to some extent, to act independently. The envelopes for Herman's money (Example 5) and Anna's alarm-clock (Example 23) are examples of that. With John (Example 9) also, it would be worth trying out if perhaps, with the help of a bowl, he could manage to measure how many carrots are needed for a salad. Or an educator may offer a young man help with tidying his room, showing him different ways to do it from which he can choose what suits him best. The idea of this kind of support is to back up a person if a task is too much for her, instead of just leaving her alone with it or taking it away from her. This way she experiences that, despite her restrictions, she is still able to do things by herself and does not just fail all the time. And the carers thus will perceive much more accurately where exactly the difficulties and limitations of a person are, where she needs support and where she is well able to act independently.

Example 27
Udo, a young man with learning disabilities, has got a new room. As he is quite independent, the carers leave it to him to unpack. He does it well and quickly, but at the end two big boxes remain lying around for weeks. Udo responds evasively to the requests of the social worker that he should finally empty the boxes and put his things into the cupboard. After a while, the social worker discovers that the boxes contain voluminous ship-models, which do not fit

into the small cupboard, but would fit on the shelves where Udo has already put other belongings. It seems that he had unpacked the boxes one after the other without thinking about what would fit in where. Now he would have to take some things from the shelves and put them into the cupboard to make space for the ship-models. To make this connection is obviously too much for him. He is just able to see that there is no space left for his ship-models. The social worker helps Udo make the necessary changes.

It would be more sensible, together with Udo, to proceed step by step: trying out where the ships fit. They fit on the shelves, so they have to clear a space there and put some things away. They go into the empty cupboard. This way Udo participates in the process and is stimulated to deal with the problem in small portions. Moreover, the carer this way discovers *where exactly* Udo's difficulties lie and can offer him a support *at the point where he gets stuck.* Solving the problem is not just taken away from Udo: he still can contribute. This is much more satisfying, not only for himself but also for the carer, as both can learn something out of it.

In old people's homes we can frequently observe that a meal is put in front of a person and, when she does not touch it, taken away after a while, often with the reproach, 'Again you did not eat, Mr. X.' Hereby carers overlook that older people, in a certain stage of decline, may still be able to make each single step — put the spoon into their mouth, swallow etc. — but no longer able to connect these steps. They need support, such as, 'Now you have to take the spoon', 'And now open your mouth', etc. The objection that this is too time-consuming does not justify the following examples, as experienced by a friend with her mother in a nursing home.

Example 28
The nurse puts a meal in front of Elizabeth, wishing her to enjoy it. When he comes later to clear away the tray, the meal is still untouched. The nurse: 'But Elizabeth, again you don't want to eat?'. Elizabeth: 'I would want to if I could.' The nurse, without a further word, takes the meal away.

It definitely had been the nurse's duty to find out which kind of support Elizabeth would need to be able to eat. Diagnostic information (like a neurological check-up) could make this task easier for the nurse. In no way can it be accepted that Elizabeth just does not eat, as she has clearly expressed that she would like to but cannot.

With others persons it is different. Some people (like Ursina in Example 24) in old age just like to eat very little. This too is an aspect of a person doing things her own way, which has to be respected. It is silly to urge her, and the reproach: 'You really have to eat' is out of place. Carers must be able to discern whether somebody does not eat because he has no appetite or because he can no longer manage it and needs support. This awareness is often missing in dealing with people in need of care — not only as far as eating is concerned.

Example 29

The nurse admonishes Elizabeth who is settled in the easy chair: 'You don't drink sufficiently, Elizabeth. If you do not drink, we have to put you on a drip.' The visiting daughter has to draw the nurse's attention to the fact, that the tea cup has been put on the bedside locker — out of Elizabeth's reach.

Frequently it is ignorance about the process of dementia but also thoughtlessness, stress or time pressure which causes such humiliating negligence, unnecessarily reinforcing the person's helplessness. It is imperative, on the organisational level, to establish the priorities differently and to take measures to avoid situations as in the example described above. (One of several possibilities could be to mobilise volunteers to assist at meals.)

Giving clear information . . .

. . . particularly if it is something unpleasant, is a necessity. Only if *the general setting is transparent* it is possible to take decisions and to make choices. Carers at first have to realise it clearly themselves, in order to make it clear for the people they take care of. The situation, as well as what will happen to people, must be transparent for all people involved. They must not be outwitted or taken by surprise, even if at the moment this seems to be easier. The mistrust created that way is much more destructive than clear information, even if it may at first raise anxiety and resistance.

The other person needs time: time to take the information in, and time to react to it. There must be space for feelings to come up, and they have to be accepted. Only then will a person be ready to cope with the situation. It is an error to think that there is no time for it: as a rule, it is just a matter of a few minutes. Moreover, carers can avoid many a fight, refusal or panic reaction which would be considerably more time-consuming and destructive.

For many people — particluarly for those with special needs — very simple situations, differing just a little from what they are used to, can be confusing and alarming. This is even more true for events completely out of daily routine which they are not able to sort out. In such cases, some clarifying words describing the situation can be extremely helpful.

Example 30

Bernard has to go to the dentist. As he panicks, this is always a difficult venture, aggravated by the unfavorably narrow position of his jaws. He can only be treated under anaesthetic, which raises even more panic. Though Bernard can barely hear, the new social worker in the evening explains to him in simple words exactly, step by step, what will happen tomorrow. (We will drive to town, see Doctor H. You will get an injection, then you will fall asleep,' etc.) The next day, Bernard, who usually reacts quite badly to much less relevant interruptions of his daily routine, without getting upset, patiently submits to the procedure.

Such information will not always be taken calmly. It may raise fear, irritation, anger and uncertainty. These feelings have to be expressed. It is very important that carers do not block or appease them, but allow and accept them empathically. At the same time they have to make it very clear that the facts this information conveys are not to be changed.

It is not always easy to accept the feelings of the other person while at the same time trying to get something done. This is equally true in educating children or in any situation when we ask or have to ask another person for something she does not like to do. We have a hard time hearing 'negative' reactions like anger, irritation and fear. We would like the other person *to be pleased* to meet our demands and — consciously or unconsciously — send out this message. This way people are encouraged, or even trained, not to admit or show their feelings, even perhaps to not perceive them at all, or only with a bad conscience and then to oppress, repress, or rationalise them. That's why it is so important, whilst not losing sight of the given facts, to respond to feelings and to take them seriously.

Looking for the concrete

Besides responding to feelings and moods, there is another level we have to pay attention to: what are the *concrete* concerns at the bottom of a person's wish or complaint? Especially with big unrealisable wishes and global complaints about things which cannot be changed, it makes sense, together with these people, more accurately to find out what they really mean, what actually they dislike or miss. Sometimes it may be quite possible to take into account a specific aspect of a desire or a complaint and thus improve or relieve a situation, which as a whole cannot be changed.

What does Hugo connect with the wish: 'I want to go home again'? Certainly it expresses how he feels after moving to the old people's home — homesick, sad, depressed or angry — and it is important to accept these feelings and take them seriously. But besides that, there may be a very concrete detail he misses or which is worrying him, which could be easily changed to make his life at the old people's home more pleasant. What is the concern behind Ruth's statement, 'I want to live somewhere else'? And what is it which depresses her colleague John who categorically declares, 'I want a new job, I don't like it anymore at the workshop'? Perhaps it is not just a matter of general dissatisfaction, but also of concrete little things which could be changed. Only after carefully checking of this can things be put right or a sensible solution be found. Perhaps it is too noisy in Ruth's flat-sharing community and she needs an opportunity to withdraw. At the workshop John possibly does not get along with the man working next to him, and it would already help him to change his place. To look for the concrete implies that 'impossible' desires are not just rejected, but taken seriously and checked to see if there is any solution. This in itself takes some of the strain off the people involved, and at the same time opens perspectives about how the concrete concerns could somehow, at least partially, be taken into account.

Example 31

A community for adults with special needs gets new furniture. The inhabitants choose it themselves. The shopping is done, and now everybody is busy setting up their rooms. All at once Mary flips and screams because the others have got a desk and she has not. She now urgently wants a desk, although when asked before she had always said that she did not want one. As she is entitled to a desk, and to stop the commotion — the transporter is still standing in front of the door — the social worker drives Mary back to the shopping centre to buy her a desk. After a week she discovers that it is still empty and Mary does not use it. It turns out that Mary needs a piece of furniture to put her cuddle toys in. For that, of course, the desk is not suitable. Yet Mary had not been able to figure that out. She just realised that there was no space for her cuddle toys and saw that the others had a desk, so she wanted to have one too.

It would have been wiser not to drive straight away to the shopping centre to meet Mary's desire, but first to find out: What *concretely* has she in mind? What does she need the desk for? And then to consider with her which piece of furniture would suit that best. Thus Mary's wish would have been met in a more sensible way and moreover she could have learned something out of it.

To look for the concrete definitely has a growth-fostering aspect to it. It is not that people are always consciously aware of their concerns and just do not talk about them. Often they only realise what they actually want when the carers, by inquiring more thoroughly, can help them to find out.

Empathic imagination may help to even find out about concrete concerns of people who do not speak. By acting out different possibilities, the carer offers the other person an opportunity to react. From these reactions he may assume her concerns, provided he succeeds to a certain extent to enter her 'language'.

Finding the other person's language

This is an important condition in order to get into contact with people with special needs. It is not sufficient for carers to *understand* the language of those they take care of; they also have to *express themselves in a way which will be understood by them.*

Sometimes carers do not realise how widely their language is determined by a professional jargon they picked up during their training and which is far removed from the way people they take care of express themselves. Yet it is frightening how often they pick up this language. Those especially with a long history as psychiatric patients frequently speak of themselves in perfect terms of psychopathology which have nothing to do with what they are experiencing.

It is not just a matter of avoiding professional jargon, but above all of finding a language the other person can understand and which is close to her experiencing. To find the language of another person implies — and *'language' here does not just mean the verbal expression, but a person's whole way of expressing herself* — explaining, making visible, describing things in a way the other person can grasp and understand. With one person, images may be appropriate; another may need logical explanations. Not always is it just a matter of 'the right words', but sometimes also of 'the right gestures'. To find another person's language can also mean taking her by the hand and doing something together.

On the other hand, a person's helplessness and speechlessness must not mislead carers to underestimate her receptivity of language. With a severely disabled woman who could not speak, a therapist discovered that she actually did react to language. She screwed up her face when the therapist said, 'I have to go now', or smiled when she promised, 'I'll see you tomorrow'. We do not know *what* this woman could take in. Was it the intonation, the emotional quality of what was said, or could she really sometimes — she did not always react — understand words? However, *something sometimes* reached her. This shows that it makes sense to talk to people who do not speak, because there is a chance that they will pick up something, and even if this may not always happen it would be a failure not to take the chance.

Also with strongly physically and mentally impaired older people who can no longer express themselves and apparently do not understand, we have to talk in a way that respects their dignity. It is a shame which can in no way be justified that there are still institutions where older people are called 'grandma' and 'grandpa'. To talk *about* persons who are present instead of *with* them is equally unacceptable.

I experienced this with a friend who died early and in her last years had to live in a nursing home. Another painful and humiliating habit is when patients are talked to as if they were not grown-up.

Example 32
Nina, 50, has got multiple sclerosis. The disease has progressed in a way that she not only cannot move but also cannot talk anymore. She has practically no possibility left to express herself. Yet when I visit her, I see in her eyes that she sensitively takes in what I am saying and is pleased when issues she had always been interested in are touched on. She is a very cultured woman who worked as an art critic before getting ill. It hurts to hear the nurses talk to her in baby language. And I can see in Nina's eyes that she definitely feels humiliated by this situation.

Knowing something about a patient's background could help nurses to strike the right note with people who cannot express themselves any more. The most important approach to the language of another person is *listening with all senses,* as has been described at the beginning of this chapter.

Recognising one's own part
I am not talking here of complex aspects of personality or personal problems which have an impact on somebody's work — this very important issue for carers will be dealt with in Chapter 6. In the context of these guidelines for everyday work I am talking very pragmatically of ways of proceeding and of the simple fact that every person involved, including the carer, has a part to play in every situation. To recognise clearly one's own part is crucial, not for the insight of 'having done something wrong' or to 'feel guilty', but in order to discover and try new options for proceeding. Sometimes, in a stressful situation, this is the only concrete clue to change something, and it usually gets a carer further than the — mostly vain — attempt to change the other person. This is particularly true for difficult situations, which escalate or happen over and over again in a similar way.

The question: 'What can *I* change in this situation?' helps to overcome helplessness and to become able again to act. We always can change *something* in our own behaviour. Here, too, it is helpful to *look for the concrete,* for clues to calm down a situation or to avoid its escalation. How did this argument start? What exactly did I say? To what did the other person react so angrily? etc. Often external conditions have an influence too: Were we alone or was somebody else present? Was the door open or closed? Was it noisy? etc. Very banal details may indicate how the carer can *somewhat* change the situation and thus give the other person a chance to also behave *somewhat* differently.

As an example, it has a quite different effect if a carer, when feeding a lame, speechless man who is resisting, tries to force the full spoon between his lips, or if she takes the spoon only after first giving him a chance to open his mouth himself. What is appropriate with one person may not be suitable for another. It is definitely worth trying different possibilities. Even if the other person is not in a position to take this little chance to change something, it is already an improvement if the carer, by changing her own way of being, *makes the situation easier for herself.* This, too, contributes to easing the tension and may open ways to improve the situation further for everybody involved.

In the following I shall point to a methodical means, which in many different ways is helpful in nearly all areas mentioned above.

Reflecting the situation . . .
. . . on the emotional and sensory level is useful — as we have seen — to respond to a person's experiencing or to help her to be more aware of it, such as, 'You don't like it when your hands get wet.' 'You are sad because nobody came to visit you today.' On the level of facts, to reflect the situation may help the involved persons to understand it better, e.g. 'It is very noisy here, because the carpenter is fixing the door.'

To reflect the situation also helps to bring a fraught situation to another level from where it is perhaps easier to find a way to calm it. Reflect the situation, especially when:
• conversations turn in circles
• power fights are going on
• aggressions escalate.

This is likely to break through the vicious circle. We could also say such things as: 'We are talking very loud now', 'I say you have to wash your hair today, you say no', 'You don't like it when it is so noisy outside', 'You feel very much like going for me right now', 'You are angry, and I am impatient', 'You are irritated that the meal is served now', etc. To reflect it takes off the tension of a situation, as it is simply stated and for the time being accepted as it is.

Reflections are sometimes misunderstood as a mechanical 'mirroring technique'. This is not at all what they are meant to be. Reflecting the situation well must be based on congruence and empathic understanding of how the other person feels. There are moments when it is not appropriate and the other person just has to be left alone. But this, too, is only possible when the carer breaks the circle, pauses for a moment and considers the situation for himself.

Reflecting the situation has to be motivated by the wish to understand and accept the other person and to communicate it to her. What is essential is the attitude behind it: it is not a matter of making a fool of or blaming somebody, but of clarifying and understanding the situation. If this comes through, changes may become possible. And it also gives the carer a breather which enables him to step back, to break the vicious circle, to stop the escalation and thus *at least to change his own part in the cycle.*

To reflect the situation can also be useful with people who don't speak: it helps the carer to step back and clarify the situation for herself — perhaps the other person who does not use language can sense that in some way.

In Garry Prouty's pre-therapy which will be introduced in Chapter 9, this principle is further developed and differentiated into a method to make contact with severely disabled and contact-impaired persons.

5

Specific aspects for the care of people with special needs[1]

In connection with the guidelines described in the last chapter, there are some additional aspects to pay attention to when working with people with moderate to severe mental disabilities.

Fostering a person's contact with her own experience
For many people with these sorts of special needs, to be in contact with their own experiencing is very difficult and *actually has to be stimulated by the carers.* Unfortunately, though not intentionally, the education of children with special needs often tends to foster incongruence more than congruence. Very rarely during their growth are they encouraged to trust their feelings, as these often are expressed in a bizarre, unintelligible way. As a rule, people around them do not make much effort to understand those odd behaviours, but spend lots of energy on stopping them.

This way people with special needs, more than others, learn to suppress or even be unaware of their feelings. As we all know, this is possible only to some degree, and pent-up emotions will occasionally break out all the more violently and inappropriately. A person with special needs will get overwhelmed by such an outburst, cannot handle it, get scared and feel guilty. The carers react even more rigidly, and the vicious circle is completed.

While more severely mentally handicapped people usually express their feelings more, this is much harder for the moderately disabled. In this respect the desire to appear 'normal' plays a sinister role: sinister because it leads people with special needs to too much adjustment and cuts them off from their emotions. Concerned about not appearing handicapped, they only show 'positive' and adjusted feelings. In no ways do they want to admit that they feel worried, irritated or angry, out of fear that these feelings might be labelled 'not normal'. And people around them, whether intentionally or not, reinforce this tendency.

1 Special needs in this chapter refer particularly to people with moderate to severe mental disabilities. See the introduction, 'About the use of language'.

Well-adjusted people with special needs who appear 'normal' are easier to deal with than those who are rebellious and let out their feelings — mostly by odd and unintelligible ways of behaving. It is easily overlooked that there is often a high price to pay for such apparently 'normal' behaviour. The person is not in contact with her emotions and her perception of self, which already is not very strong, weakens even more.

Example 33

Irene, a woman of 60, who is in therapy with me, expresses her feelings mostly in indirect ways by accusing others. Only after several years can she express how irritated and angry she feels, because her cousin talks to her as if she were a child. Up to then, she had only dared to criticise him for not speaking the dialect spoken in his native area, but having taken on the dialect of his wife. This was the language of Irene's childhood, which she hated and had refused to speak ever since her mother died and she had been moved to another town.

Irene could not admit the anger against her cousin as her own subjective feeling, but had to find some apparently objective 'wrong behaviour' in order to justify her criticism. We frequently observe this kind of shift, and not only in people with special needs. Recalling the theory of the self-concept (p.12), we can easily assess the impact this splitting off her feelings and experiences has on her growth. To have little or no contact with one's own emotions is one of the main reasons for psychological disorders and for difficulties in coping with life.

People with special needs usually mistrust their own experience because over and over again it had not been understood, but dismissed as inadequate or unrealistic by the people around them. Sometimes this goes so far that they are not even aware of how they experience and sense things, but fall back on platitudes and on what they hear others say.

Example 34

When I ask Irene if she likes the new job at the workshop, she answers, 'I always work hard.' Or when the question is discussed whether, because of her age, she would like to stop working or prefer to continue, she says, 'At the workshop they still appreciate my help.'

I only can try, again and again, to gently stimulate Irene's contact with her own experiencing: 'You were pleased', 'You don't like this so much', 'Now it gets too much for you'. The hope is that this will slowly open up this dimension and make it more accessible for her, yet above all, not adding even more to her distance to her own feelings and sensations. Quite ordinary everyday situations can be used to call someone's attention to the experiencing quality, and also to the fact that this is not the same for everybody: 'You don't like rain. Anna enjoys the rain,' 'You get scared when Eva laughs like this', 'You don't like the noise of the vacuum cleaner, Mark likes it', etc.

A crucial factor is how carers deal with their own feelings, as it has a model function for those in their care and helps them better to perceive and express their feelings themselves. This is particularly true for 'negative' feelings like anger, rage, irritation, weariness etc. It is important for people with special needs to see that carers too are sometimes angry, depressed, or sad and that they admit these feelings. This makes it easier for them to admit such feelings in themselves. Of course, it has to happen in a constructive way. Carers must not use their feelings to pressure the other person or to make her feel guilty, but give an example of how such emotions are part of being human and can be lived with and expressed without being overwhelmed.

People with special needs usually have a hard time accepting 'negative' feelings; they feel guilty when, nevertheless, these break through.

Example 35

Armin tells me about a fierce argument he had with his boss at the workshop this afternoon. He accuses himself bitterly of 'not being able to explain things in a way people can understand'. When I ask him if he was irritated because Mrs H did not understand him, he gives me a startled look and says, 'But one should not think such a thing.' During another session he expresses his fears of 'flipping' during the coming vacation because this had happened during the last vacation. He had been tired of being away, did not feel good any more and had wished to go home. 'I have to tell myself, this time always be happy,' he firmly declares. I try carefully to help him understand that it is impossible to be just happy all the time, and that perhaps it would be better to tell the facilitators when he feels homesick or depressed, instead of swallowing it and then probably 'flipping' precisely because of that.

This example, once more, demonstrates how essential it is that carers empathically pay attention to and accept those moods and feelings. Often they have a hard time with it, because they try their best and feel responsible for the well-being of the people they take care of. This responsibility is more than they can cope with: even the best possible caring cannot prevent somebody occasionally not feeling well or being sad or annoyed. If carers are aware of this it not only helps the concerned person, but also contributes to avoiding escalations and dramatic outbursts which are unpleasant and sometimes scaring for everybody. Moreover, this way people with special needs learn to be more aware of their feelings. It is a process which takes time: it takes more time the greater a person's alienation from her experiencing, the roots of which often go back to childhood. By encouraging a child to be aware of and to accept his emotions and experiences the early years could have different outcomes.

But it is not just in terms of their emotions that people with special needs have few opportunities to build up self-confidence. In matters of daily life too, again and again they experience 'I cannot do it', or 'I am doing it the wrong way'. This marks their self-concept in a way that makes them forget how to trust their experience, and they orient themselves exclusively on what is communicated to them as 'adequate'. And as there are indeed many things they cannot do or they do the wrong way, their behaviour from early on is constantly corrected. Sometimes this is done much more than necessary, because people around them wish them to appear as 'normal' as possible, forgetting how important it is that people with special needs, wherever possible, try out their own ways, even if their behaviour then may not quite conform to the norm. They anyway have to be corrected more than enough in situations where indeed it is impossible to follow their impulses. So they forget more and more how to perceive their own impulses, sensations and reactions or dismiss them straightaway as 'not normal'.

Stimulate a person's own impulses
With a mentally handicapped person, it is not enough to just support her independence; her own impulses have actually to be stimulated and encouraged. Daily life offers countless opportunities to do so. Clothing, for example, is a large field. It is alarming how sometimes, from the way people with special needs are dressed, the taste of the staff can be detected.

Example 36
Lucy is very concerned to dress in a way to please people around her. On weekends, when she goes home, she dresses to reflect her mother's taste (which is considered awful by the staff); on weekdays she wears the clothes she thinks would please the staff. Looking at her wardrobe, it is easy to make out which piece of clothing has been bought with which staff member.

The staff could counteract that by not just being content when their clients adapt to their taste, but encouraging them to find out *what they like themselves.* For example, instead of saying: 'This sweater does not go with the trousers you wear', they could let Lucy look at the mirror and try out with her: 'How do you like yourself better, this way or that way?'. It is necessary to emphasise, again and again, that not everybody has to have the same taste, for instance by saying: 'I like this one, John likes the other one, which one do you like?'.

Example 37

In an adult education programme for people with special needs, the participants do a role-play on how to buy clothes. A week later, Paul's mother tells the facilitator that she had to buy Paul a dark sweater for a funeral. They went from shop to shop, and finally Paul had to decide between two sweaters. Both the mother and the shopkeeper suggested the darker one, which would better suit the occasion and in which they thought Paul looked better. But Paul insisted on the other, a flashy, bright blue sweater. Asked why, he said, 'Because it feels so soft when I touch it'.

To provide such experiences does not necessarily need external programmes. It can easily be integrated in the social activities of the institution or community. For example, entertaining and yet instructive plays with clothes and cloths could be arranged, offering people an opportunity to try out, to look in a mirror, to look at each other and to share their different tastes. This could be a relaxing as well as exciting alternative to the sometimes rather hectic and overloaded leisure programmes provided for people with special needs.

These programmes could be built more upon the idea of *providing opportunities for experiences and developing people's awareness of their own sensations, tastes and opinions.* Any excursion or shopping trip may help to stimulate individual perceptions and views. People with special needs usually have a strong tendency to adapt to what is considered 'nice'. This should not be reinforced: instead they should be encouraged not to dismiss straight away as 'not normal' what they perceive and feel, but to take it seriously, even if it is different from how they think it should be.

By this I do not mean that the fact of being disabled should be denied or covered up. It is a reality to be accepted, yet a reality with many different facets which are easily overlooked if our eyes remain fixed on the label 'special needs'.

The attitude towards being disabled . . .

. . . is a complex problem with which people with special needs are constantly confronted — sometimes in quite contradictory ways. On the one hand their carers would like to see them as much 'adapted' as possible, and on the other hand are they expected to accept their being disabled. This is no small demand on people with special needs who, being disabled, are perhaps just therefore not in a position to meet this expectation. Even more so, wherever they go they are confronted with discrimination at stores, on the bus, at the swimming pool, on the street. No wonder many of them tend to deny as much as they can their being handicapped, and try to keep a distance from other people with special needs. For more severely disabled persons it seems easier, because they are probably less conscious of their being handicapped. But they, too, are very sensitive to the reactions of other people and do sense that they are not how they 'should' be.

In this respect again, *the attitude of the carers* has a crucial impact. It largely determines how people they take care of can live with their being handicapped. To accept it is possible only if they can also experience *positive aspects* of their being as they are. For that they need support and encouragement from the carers, and this requires *being able to see* such positive aspects.

To take people with special needs seriously does not mean overlooking their handicaps, but *to take them seriously with their handicaps.* In the effort — in itself commendable — not to discriminate against people with special needs, this sometimes is forgotten. Undifferentiated 'political correctness' can have the opposite effect to what has been intended, as the following example demonstrates.

Example 38

Nineteen-year-old Betty lives with her parents. She spends three days a week in a day care facility offering special programmes for people with special needs, and on two days she goes to school. From where she lives, there is no public transport to these places, therefore the social services so far had paid for a taxi. But with ongoing austerity measures, these contributions will be cut and other solutions have to be found. Together with her parents, Betty is invited to a meeting. As she is over 18, she has a right to be informed personally and to give her view. The social worker has prepared a paper which describes the situation and which for half an hour she tries to explain to Betty in detail. She does not realise that Betty is neither able to follow these explanations nor able to listen for such a long stretch of time. Yet, when asked if she did understand, Betty's answer is 'yes'. Several alternatives to the actual situation are discussed. After that Betty is asked again if she did understand, and again she says 'yes'. The social worker does not realise that Betty did not understand anything and just said 'yes' because she felt awkward and wanted to put the situation to an end. At home, when asked by her mother why she had said 'yes', Betty says, 'What else could I do?', which shows how, emotionally, she quite accurately had grasped the situation she was in. As it turns out, the only result of the meeting is that Betty now thinks she cannot go to the day care facility any more. She is very upset and desperate, because she likes it there and sees the facility as her second home.

This despair could have been spared Betty if the social worker had not just taken into account her being old enough, but also her limited abilities to understand. Although acting with best intentions and wanting to take Betty seriously, she definitely lacked the necessary empathy in Betty's frame of reference. Yet, without this empathy, the needs of people with special needs cannot be met. To expect too much of them is as counter-productive as to not believe enough in them. Again, it is a matter of finding the adequate balance, which for each person is different.

People with special needs, like everybody else, have to learn how to live with their weak sides. But carers must also make it possible for them to experience and recognise their strong sides and capabilities. Emphasis should not be so much on the label 'special needs' as on individual *strong and weak sides* — their own and those of others, including the carers — and on learning to deal with them. To recognise that other people have their specific capabilities and limitations too, to discover that human beings are different and to learn to accept these differences, is an imperative condition for a tolerable way people with special needs can live with each other and with the people around them.

We do need to discriminate between different kinds and grades of special needs, but we should be very careful about using labels like more handicapped, less handicapped, stronger than others, weaker than others. People with special needs tend to adopt those labels themselves to sort out each other and to establish a hierarchy of handicaps where they see themselves as high up as possible. This, of course, does not foster good relations with each other.

Example 39
For Irene it is very important to what degree the other women in her community are handicapped. She is very happy to tell of one of her friends, 'She belongs to the weaker group', or of another, 'She gets fits and has to take medication, I don't'. It was terrible for her when a few years ago, after an accident, she had to move to a group of more severely disabled women. It is not relevant for her if she feels better or worse there: what counts is the blemish, 'I now belong to a weaker group.'

It is disturbing to see, as in the example above, the negative effects this sort of labelling can have. It would be much more constructive if carers would try to encourage people who have to live together to be aware of and to tolerate differences in human beings, and to show this awareness and tolerance by example. People with special needs must be encouraged to benefit from the strong sides and to balance the weak sides of each other. They should be given opportunities to look at their own strengths and those of others and to see where they *need* help and where they *can offer* help to others. In addition to mutual help, this attitude facilitates independence from the carers and stimulates friendship among people with special needs.

Yet for all this stressing positive aspects, we cannot ignore *that people with special needs sometimes deeply suffer from being disabled* even if they cannot always express it as clearly as in the following example.

Example 40

Elsa, usually a lively and cheerful woman, during the therapy session suddenly bursts out crying bitterly: 'I wish I could fly away like a little bird, far far away . . . and nothing . . . nothing at all . . . only whistle nice little songs . . . I am a dirty rag . . . just a dirty rag . . . I am nothing, nothing, nothing . . . nothing at all, that's what I am.' To try to comfort and appease her is out of place. The only thing I can do is to respond to her feelings and bear them with her until they ease and there is room again for other things. I am strongly aware of my helplessness and feel a little embarrassed as Elsa, after the session, hugs me and says, 'You really helped me.'

This example, once more, clearly demonstrates how essential it is in such a situation to just empathically be there and support the person. Carers often have a hard time just to 'be there'. Such emotional outbursts of their clients strongly confront them with their own helplessness and limitations. To 'be there' is not an easy task, but in those situations it helps a person more than anything else does, because it makes space for her emotions and encourages her to express them.

It is not pleasant to be handicapped — this fact cannot be denied or whitewashed. People with special needs now and then feel that very painfully, even if rarely somebody is able to express it as impressively as Elsa did. Yet those who cannot express themselves verbally probably sometimes have similar feelings. How does a woman feel who is hardly able to move, and cannot speak and eat by herself? Could it be an expression of her distress about this condition not to open her mouth and to refuse being fed by a new carer she does not know? We do not know, but depend on empathic guesses to get an idea of what could be going on within her.

In that respect our own feelings may serve as a signpost. Carers too, in some situations, feel helpless, sad, angry, weary, disgusted and may curse the fact that people have to live with such handicaps. Usually such feelings and thoughts are suppressed because they 'should not be'. But as suppressed feelings are not controllable and will, at some point, break through anyway, this helps neither the carers nor the people they take care of, who thus are confirmed in having to hide their feelings. Whereas if carers are consciously aware of those emotions in themselves, not only will their psychological well-being benefit, but they may also discover a clue for better understanding the person who has given rise to those feelings.

Sexuality and relationships

In this area, people with special needs particularly experience the distress of being disabled. Although, fortunately, the attitude towards sexuality of people with special needs has become much more liberal in the last few decades, the question if and how they can have relationships and acknowledge their sexuality remains a difficult and often insoluble problem. Even if these feelings are tolerated or encouraged by a community, which is rare, the possiblities are still limited. Various factors play their part in it, including society, philosophy, personality, personal development, actual situation etc. Is it possible at all, in everyday life, to deal with this complex issue in a person-centred way?

It is a tight-rope walk, in the area of relationships to handle structure and self-determination in a way that respects individual freedom and the right for love, friendship and sexuality of a person with special needs and at the same time protects her from dangers like violence, AIDS, unwanted pregnancy etc. There is no magic formula. Each person, each situation, is different and has carefully to be looked at and thought over.

First we have to clarify what those concerned really want. What do they expect of a relationship, what are their options, and what is the general setting? We have to find out sensitively and individually what *concretely* a person is looking for. Carers have a tendency to transfer their own ideas and ideals of relationships onto the people they take care of, and to work from standards which are not always fit for them. If even 'normal' couples are only rarely able to really meet such high ideals, how difficult must it be for people with special needs! Although in terms of relationships their desire to 'be normal' is particularly strong, and notions like 'going steady', 'being engaged', or 'being married' have a nearly magic attraction, it is often not at all clear what they concretely have in mind. Therefore it is not of much use to force their relationships into norms which often even 'normal' couples don't think they can cope with. How should people with special needs be expected to meet such high ideals — apart from the fact that often it is not what they really need? These real needs should first be carefully clarified.

Instead of talking of 'going steady', of engagement or even marriage, and then leaving it to them to come to terms with the ideas they connect with these notions, alternatives should be developed. Here again, it is helpful to look for the concrete. What exactly do these two people expect from their relationship? What would they like and what would they not like? Where do the expectations of both partners conform and where do they differ? Carers should, together with those concerned, carefully find that out, and then look for other ways in which these two people could handle their relationship, according to their specific needs and possibilities. The most important thing is to stay absolutely *concrete and pragmatic*, and not to let oneself be guided by ideas of how it 'should' be.

Example 41

Erna and Eric 'go steady'. Soon Eric wants to 'break off'. The carers try to talk him out of that. They are afraid it could be a bad setback for Erna 'not to go with Eric anymore'. The consultant suggests that the carers should find out from Eric what exactly it means for him 'not to go together anymore'. What is it concretely that Eric does not want? It turns out that Eric feels pressed when Erna, without asking, comes to his room whenever she likes. (For Erna this is part of 'going steady'.) But he still likes to kiss and cuddle and go out with her sometimes. Instead of a hard 'either/or', 'go steady' or 'break off', there have to be found other ways and clear agreements made for their being together, going out with each other once or twice a week, for example. And Erna should not just go into Eric's room, but ask him if it is okay and accept that he may sometimes say no. Eric, on the other hand, should not just wait for Erna to ask and then say yes or no, but occasionally himself ask Erna if she would like to come to his room.

The structure of an institution or community can provide a sheltered space where various forms of relationship are possible, according to the needs of the inhabitants. To find out concretely and clearly what two persons want from each other and what they don't want, and make the respective agreements, is far more constructive than the label 'engaged' or 'going steady', not least because, when needs change, these agreements can be modified without inevitably leading to breaking off the relationship. Moreover, in this way people with special needs learn to recognise more clearly and more concretely what they really want, instead of sticking to a status like 'engaged' or 'married' — a status which is likely to develop a momentum of its own, too difficult for them to live up to.

Example 42

John and Liz are engaged. They are very proud of it, as it had been duly celebrated in the institution and grants them a higher status. Soon they can form a small flat-sharing community together with Werner, another man with special needs, and move to their own apartment. This is the beginning of difficulties. It is the rule in flat-sharing communities that all inhabitants, men and women, equally have to share the housework. John shirks whenever he can; he is engaged now, and in his mind it is the woman's task to do the housework for both. Liz thinks so too, so she does the housework for them all, as Werner does not see either why he, as a man, should do housework when John does not. Even though the carers try to counteract these traditional male–female roles, as soon as they leave the house, Liz, without a word, takes over the tasks of the men. Although she feels that this is how it has to be, very soon it gets too much for her, and she often gets bad-tempered or depressed. And soon John's sexual demands too get too much for her, and she wishes she had her own room again. But for a long time she does not dare to say so because, for her, it means to 'break off the engagement' — a humiliating failure in her eyes. For a long time the term 'engagement' was in the way of any change and hindered a solution being found to which both could agree and which matched their changed needs.

They would have more easily come to terms with the changes in their relationship which for them were connected with 'breaking off the engagement' and like a stigma, if they could have worked out other, more appropriate ways of being together. As people with special needs, particularly the mildly handicapped, have so much longing to be like 'normal people', they doubly experience it as a failure when they cannot cope with what counts as the norm.

Not always is the wish to be in a relationship a matter of sexuality, and not always is the desire for sexual contacts connected with a need to be in a close relationship. Here again, carers should put aside their own values and find out what it is exactly the concerned people want.

There is still the idea around that people with special needs are particularly sex driven. Very rarely is this true. Experience shows that couples with special needs are often much more interested in closeness, tenderness, touching and cuddling than in sexual intercourse. However, there are of course people with special needs who enjoy and feel a need for sexual contacts, be it within or without a steady relationship.

Example 43

Daisy, a 30-year-old woman with Down's Syndrome is in therapy with me. At a meeting the carers express their concern, because Daisy had apparently more or less been forced into sexual contact by a friend. I am somewhat surprised because Daisy, talking of this friend, never had mentioned such an incident, nor had she in any way appeared distraught or depressed. In the next session I cautiously asked questions. It turned out that, for some time, when she used to see her friend regularly, they did have sexual contact which Daisy did not at all dislike. On the contrary, she had very much enjoyed these physical sensations and is disappointed that she is no longer allowed to visit her friend as often as before. But from the way she was brought up, as well as from the reactions of the carers, she felt that she has done something 'bad'. She did not dare to admit her pleasure in these sexual contacts, but claimed that they had happened against her will. She had sensed exactly what the carers wanted to hear her say. For them, sexual contacts were unacceptable outside a stable relationship. They did not see that Daisy was neither interested in, nor probably up to, such a relationship, but simply enjoyed the sexual experience.

Opinions are divided on whether such relations can or have to be tolerated. I think that we don't have the right to just transfer our own ideas of morality and values on people with special needs, thus restricting their already limited opportunities in this area even more. I think we should accept when their standards and feelings differ from our ideas of relationships, which as a matter of fact are individually quite different too.

People with special needs have so little opportunities to live their sexuality that we should not deny them the few chances that come up, as long as it does not intimidate or endanger anybody. We also need to be tolerant towards compensations like fetishism or sex magazines etc. But the consideration that nobody else gets harmed and the safety of the persons concerned should be the criteria for tolerating or not tolerating a situation; not the personal values of the carers.

To protect this safety is not an easy task. Under the sign of AIDS and increasing sexual violence, it is not enough just to provide contraception. Restrictions cannot always be avoided. And again, mildly handicapped people who particularly resent restrictions are most affected.

Example 44

Sabina is a 44-year-old, mildly mentally handicapped woman. She lives in a flat-sharing community and loves to go out in the evening. She frequents pubs where they play music. She feels good there, not only because she likes the music, but also because in this milieu she is not so much noticed as being disabled. There does not seem to be much difference between her and the other people there, and she is treated as an equal. One night she comes home, rather excited, and reports to the carer that a man had wanted to invite her to his home, but that she did not go. Quite obviously, she would have liked to, but was not sure if it was 'allowed'. The carer too is not sure about how to react. She does not want to patronise Sabina, but she is afraid that something could happen. There is a risk that a man who approaches her in a pub could get violent, once she goes home with him. She tells her fears to Sabina who promises that in the future she will never go home with a man. The carer does not feel good about the way she handled the situation. She has the impression that she manipulated Sabina and that the problem was not satisfactorily resolved.

As the carer, at that moment, could not think of any solution, it was certainly congruent to admit her fears. But probably in the long run other solutions should be found. For example, a rule could be set that new acquaintances should first be invited to the community for a coffee or a meal, so that carers get to know them and can form an impression. The fact that he does or does not accept such an invitation in itself is a statement. But there is, of course, no guarantee and risks can never totally be excluded.

For the carers it is a balancing act between taking risks in order to respect the personal freedom of someone with special needs and make relationshiops possible for her, imposing the necessary restrictions to protect her from dangers. Besides, carers are often bound by legal regulations. Yet restrictions based upon real necessities are definitely more honest and easier to cope with, even if they are painful, than restrictions based on personal standards of the carers, often not understandable for the people they take care of.

The difficult demands of living in a group
To live in a group, particularly if it is not chosen, makes high demands on the social capabilities of people with special needs. This paradox usually is not sufficiently considered. On the one hand they are declared handicapped and limited in their social capabilities, and on the other hand they are quite naturally expected to adjust, have regard and understanding for the people they have to live with, to a degree most 'normal' people would hardly be willing to achieve.

To find their way in the group takes up a lot of a person's energy and learning ability — resources they otherwise might use better for their personal growth. Moreover, what has been achieved after considerable effort, time and again is jeopardised by a new situation (such as new residents or new staff members). Such a change requires new adjustments and makes new demands. This is asking much of people with special needs who otherwise are not credited with much capabilities, and it is amazing what they can achieve in this respect. But sometimes they are just totally stressed. This is often the real root of much inadequate behaviour, panicking or 'flipping'. It would be wise, sometimes, to lower the demands and look for solutions which would take some strain off the person, even if this does not conform with 'group ideals', usually based more on theoretical ideas of the carers than on the real needs of the people they take care of.

I ask myself more and more if it would not suit some people with special needs better to live in *a sort of boarding house where they are looked after individually,* instead of having to live in a group which is not beneficial for everybody. Of course inhabitants of such a boarding house should not be just left to fend for themselves. There should be programmes for common leisure activities in which they could choose to participate if they want to. Intense, but not necessarily time-consuming, individual care has to be built in. Carers could, for example, at fixed times be present and available to listen to and, if necessary, help and consult inhabitants. This could also offer new challenges and allow other priorities for the carers, who often complain that they need too much time and energy to organise routines and settle conflicts in the group and that there is not enough space for individual care.

Such ideas are certainly no magic formula. Each way of living has its specific problems. Yet, I believe that, in addition to existing concepts, options as described above could be useful and really meet the needs of many adult, particularly older, people with special needs.

6
Consequences for carers

What are the specific demands of person-centred work? What effects has this attitude on the self-image of carers and on their relationships with the people they take care of? And how do they themselves benefit from working this way?

The relationship to the clients
The relationship between carers and clients is essential not only for the person-centred approach. There is common agreement that it is a major aspect of social work. Yet ideas of how this relationship should be differ widely and sometimes are not very clear. It is worth thinking about more thoroughly.

From a person-centred point of view the relationship between carers and clients (just as the therapeutic relationship in client-centred therapy) is based on empathy, acceptance and congruence. Congruence implies that the specific characteristics of this relationship, as well as its limitations, have to be clear and transparent for everybody involved. It is, to some degree, a one-sided relationship where the priority is on the clients' well-being and on encouraging their independence. *Their* needs must be met, *their* living spaces created, not those of the carers whose private life takes place elsewhere.

For the staff *it is a job* living with people with special needs or in need of care. After work they go back to their homes and live their own private life. This fact is frequently blurred: carers try to establish a very close personal relationship with clients and raise desires they cannot meet. Very soon they may be burnt out and have to look for another job. For people with special needs this means, once more, that they are abandoned and disappointed — an experience they know only too well. Depending on their different personalities, they try in different ways to protect themselves from such let-downs; some by persistently clinging to the carers in the hope that this will hold them; others, on the contrary, by refusing any relationship and resisting the closeness the carers try to offer them.

It gets particularly problematic when carers use the relationship with their clients to meet their own unfulfilled needs or unsolved problems. Whether those needs are for recognition, closeness, affection, tenderness, power, or the unrealised wish for their own children or other aspects of life carers did not come to terms with, to transfer it on people they take care of is definitely an abuse (even when there is no sexual harassment involved — which unfortunately happens sometimes too).

Example 45

In a nursing school, teachers are on very friendly terms with their students. They are tolerant, do not pressure their performance, show an interest in their personal difficulties and, after school hours, frequently socialise with them. Then the exams come up, and the students are flabbergasted as, all of a sudden, the teachers are not that understanding any more but severely judge and grade their performances. Instead of, right from the start, making clear demands, the teachers, by being too friendly, had blurred the fact that, under the circumstances, the relationship could not be equal, as they had to grade the students and make decisions that affect their future.

More distance would have been more appropriate to the situation and ultimately more helpful for the students. It is a fatal misunderstanding to confuse the person-centred attitude with simply 'being nice'. Congruence, among other things, entails not blurring a professional context.

In this work, *a reliable professional relationship,* which keeps some distance but provides continuity, is fare more honest. It serves staff and clients better than too much closeness, which afterwards suddenly is given up because it gets too much for the carer to keep up. As affectionate, warm and caring it may be, it has to be clear for everybody that it is a professional relationship. Professional does not mean cold or unconcerned, nor does it imply mechanical routine. Professional means that the carers' priorities are concentrated on the well-being and growth of their clients, not on their own desires for closeness or for being needed. It may sometimes happen that a carer pays particular attention to a person if it is necessary for her personal growth — yet it is also necessary, when the time comes, to facilitate and encourage the process of detachment, in order not to establish a permanent dependency. Only in this way does it make sense and is justifiable for carers to offer 'family-like' relationships.

Being professional means:
• that the relationship conforms to the professional context and the tasks of the persons involved

- that the needs of the clients are the focus of attention and that their idiosyncrasy is respected and encouraged
- that carers, in relationships with clients, set aside their own needs, ambitions and ideas
- that dependencies are minimised.

Even though these criteria apply to all staff members, each relationship will be unique and have its own distinct nature. Different carers will of course have better relationships with some of those in their care than others. But it should never go so far that the staff's positive or negative feelings for the clients result in privileges or disadvantages. To give an extreme example, it is not tolerable that in a facility for homeless people an extremely difficult, abandoned and constantly railing man is refused a meal by some staff members, whereas from others he gets it.

Not personal standards of good behaviour, but rather a clearly defined general setting, transparent and beneficial for everybody, should be the deciding factor on how to act. Only in this way will the clients experience continuity and stability. If the same kind of relationship is granted *continuously,* if people can trust that *everybody in the staff works along the same lines,* they can cope more easily with frequently changing carers.

Demands . . .
What are the specific demands, besides regular professional requirements, that person-centred work makes on carers? They are certainly not fundamentally different or fundamentally new. But the person-centred concept sets other priorities, the assessments are different and this implies *a different conception of themselves on the part of the carers.* Not 'I know what's best for the other person', but 'I can try to help her find her own best way'. It is not so much a matter of 'making' than of 'facilitating'. Therefore the achievement of carers will not always be so obvious — which sometimes is hard to cope with for the carers as well as for the people around. If we were to exaggerate we could say that the more dispensable a carer *appears,* the better her work is. It's not what she is visibly doing that is essential, but *what she makes possible for the people she takes care of.* It is not a familiar way of working to many, and we have first to get used to it. It is also more demanding for the staff which may not seem evident at first sight.

It certainly does not mean that carers should not use their creative skills and the methods they have learned. But they should keep them in the background, available as possibilities to be used when the situation and the needs of a client require it. Priority is not on the method as such, or on using it as much as possible, but on the other person — for whom this method may or may not be useful. This difference is crucial as it shows quite dramatically in the example of the psychologist Barbara Krietemeyer working with severely handicapped Laura (see Chapter 12, 'A hopeless case?').

Empathy, sensitivity and interest in other human beings are fundamentals in this work, indispensable for enabling carers to take their clients seriously, to find their language and to respond to their experiencing. To trust possibilities of growth requires *flexibility* not to stick to what is already known of a person but to stay open for changes, for new and unexpected behaviours. *Empathic imagination* is needed to develop programmes facilitating new experiences, encouraging independence and creating space for the decisions of those taken care of.

To encourage the other person's own way implies *carers should be ready to let go of their own ideas.* To offer choices also means *to accept choices we would not make ourselves.* To credit other people's personal responsibility implies *to give responsibility away.* Professionals in the social field often have a hard time with that. They are so much used to thinking and acting for other people — and actually very often have to — that they tend to take over *all* responsibility and not to see the, perhaps just tiny, areas where it is not opportune. Not only do they restrict their clients more than necessary, they also cause themselves stress. This is one of the factors leading to the burn-out syndrome.

The person-centred attitude requires not just empathy but also congruence and this, above all, makes *demands on the carer as a person.* To be willing to reflect one's own person and work is part of it. Carers must learn to recognise and modify their own part in a situation, to be conscious of their own ideas, inclinations, fears, problems, reactions and concerns and to separate them from what they perceive in the other person. Carers need to be aware of their own blind spots. Their personal life must be somehow balanced and provide the necessary compensations for their often stressful work as well as the base where they recover and regenerate. If need be, counselling or psychotherapy may offer helpful support on this score.

. . . and benefits
Are these demands not too much? Do they not put even more strain on the carers whose work is difficult and demanding enough? I believe that the contrary is true. If clients experience being listened and responded to, if they feel understood by their carers, they will be more content and more co-operative. There will be less power fights and less

aggressive and rebellious behaviours — which certainly makes life easier for the carers. It is a relief, for example, if a severely handicapped man does not soil himself or lash out so often anymore. Consequently the danger that worn out and enervated carers get violent themselves will diminish as well.

In particular, the necessity of coming to terms with themselves is not only a demand, but also a benefit for the carers, *a chance for personal growth and taking good care of themselves.* To be consciously aware of and admit feelings, even when 'negative', helps to recognise in time and do something to prevent being overstretched. Moreover, strengths will be set free which before had been absorbed by the blocking of emotions.

The person-centred attitude is not only directed towards other people, but also towards oneself. It is equally important for carers to accept themselves as they are, with all their weak and strong sides, as to meet their clients with this attitude. To work in a person-centred way offers the chance to discover and benefit from personal resources, but also for making work easier for themselves and — within the given conditions and tasks — doing it their own best way. There are sometimes situations where it is legitimate to ask, 'What can I do to make it more tolerable for myself?' It is crucial, though, that the carer then is honest about it and does not pretend to be doing it for the other person. This too is part of congruence.

To act with restraint does not imply to limit oneself with taboos and restrictions. It means to take a step back and create a space, not only for the other person, but also for oneself. New perspectives will open up and fresh impulses are freed, livening up the monotony of everyday work; to change the point of view helps to break a dull routine. This shift of viewpoint at first may perhaps not be so easy for the carers, but in the long term, I am sure, they will experience it as a relief and a reward. Looking for new ways, being open to potential growth, turning away from dull routine makes work more interesting and satisfying.

This is clearly confirmed by Maria Schmucki[1] who in a nursing home works with 'validation' (see Chapter 11), a method showing parallels to the person-centred approach. She wrote an interesting paper on this issue, and in an interview told me, 'There is this very withdrawn woman, bitter in a way and totally passive — there is a danger that we do everything for her and that she becomes just an object. I don't like that, it leaves me dissatisfied. But if I am aware, "Here she is, and here am I, and she is like me a human being, and when I include her, look at her and talk to her, then she sometimes looks at me too", something happens and somehow we meet each other, and I am much more satisfied with my work. If I can find access to a person, if a relationship comes into being, this is very rewarding for me too.'

Harry Hulskers, whose task as hospital consultant, among others, is to convey humanistic care concepts to the nurses, in our interview reports a similar experience: 'Nursing care gets more alive, and work is experienced as more interesting. It is not satisfying just to connect patients with diagnosis and surgery.'

Often professionals express their concern that in daily routine there is no time to work this way. This is a fallacy. *To work in a person-centred way does not take more time, but probably will, in the end, save time.* To be listened to for a minute is for the client as well as for the carer of more use than the carer being half present for fifteen minutes, with his mind already on the next duty. Infinite time and energy is consumed by misunderstandings and useless power fights. To concentrate fully on a person for a moment, and then to turn fully to the other task for a moment, does not take more time, but requires working differently with the available time. Responding to a person has priority over chores, which may as well be done tomorrow or for once a little less carefully than usual.

'For instance,' says Maria Schmucki, 'it is not necessary in a nursing home to every day completely wash an aged person. If somebody really wants that, it makes sense. But most people don't want it. And it takes so much time and energy. The personal hygiene may easily be spread over different days, and perhaps they can get a bath or a shower from time to time and everyday what they really need. This gives us a lot of time.'

And she realises how essential her inner attitude is: 'If I can admit calm myself, then there is space for it. It works, it changes something, and it is effective. I should not let myself be rushed. If I am calm and relaxed, I can perceive much better what is going on around me and respond to the other person more adequately. At first I adjusted and let myself be rushed. But then I started to do my work in a way I thought was good, and it was amazing how at once everything was far more relaxed, I got through with everything and did not need more time. I worked with a different attitude. This caused such a calming down and was much more satisfying. I got a lot out for myself by working this way. And it was the same for other colleagues who tried it too.'
Relaxed, motivated staff and contented clients are a benefit also for the

institution, and it would be a good idea if institutions would support ways of working which facilitate this. In which way and to what extent person-centred work is possible largely depends on the importance the concept is given by the institution.

7

Institutional attitudes to the person-centred concept

The attitude of the institution to the person-centred concept is crucial to its successful implementation. From the viewpoint of organisational development it would be desirable to intruduce a specifically designed person-centred concept for each level and area of the institution, according to its general setting. Continuity and a common base would be best achieved by including the whole institution. This is easier to realise in small communities than in big organisations where, by nature, extensive changes will run into more difficulties.

Therefore it is realistic also to consider partial solutions. It may absolutely make sense, at first, to introduce the person-centred concept just in a small unit — like a group, a house, a ward (see Chapter 10, 'A psychiatric ward in Belgium') or a department — in order to gain experience which later may be used to include further areas of the institution. The necessary condition is that the staff involved in the unit really put some effort into the person-centred approach, and that they are positive about this way of working and willing to learn more about it. New staff members must get precise information about the approach and also be prepared to work that way.

Carers often start a new job with great enthusiasm, endowed with plenty of new ideas they want, with the best intentions, to try out on the residents. Only rarely does this lead to the desired results. Those staff members already working there are mostly sceptical about such experiments. And the clients usually react with confusion and withdrawal when suddenly being confronted with new ideas which had not been developed out of empathically understanding them within their frame of reference. They are resistant, and the new carer is disappointed. He will perhaps struggle for a while and then give up and resign.

The institution could prevent such confusions by having a clear concept and by giving applicants detailed informationabout it, so that they know what is expected from them and can decide whether or not they want to let themselves into it. If in an institution, or a school, or a group, work is firmly based on the person-centred concept, and if the described foundations are the guidelines for the staff, many counter-productive and demotivating experiments could be avoided which otherwise use up a big part of the energy and goodwill of carers as well as of the people they take care of. For the clients, a clear concept makes sure that new carers will not turn everything upside down. For the staff, it defines the framework within which it makes sense to direct their energy and develop ideas. If people know where they stand, they can be spared much confusion.

There are four determining factors for useful person-centred work in an institution:
• support from the management
• the way the concept is introduced
• clear and adequate organisational structures
• consultation and supervision.

Support by the management
Regardless of the size of the organisation intending to work with this concept it needs the unequivocal support of the management, otherwise the concept has little chance of being successful. The organisation basically needs to feel positive about a humanistic 'conception of man'. The management must know about the fundamentals of the person-centred approach and be convinced of their importance for practice. It has to support the staff in its orientation on person-centred guidelines and provide necessary supports like supervision, consultation and training opportunities.

The management must also be in a position to advocate clearly the person-centred concept externally towards relatives, authorities and committees, as well as internally towards the staff. Transparency is crucial, especially if in a big institution only a particular department works this way. Any departments which are not involved also have to be informed about what is going on. This way mistrust can be diminished and openness for change encouraged. A big part of its success is the way the concept is introduced.

Introducing the person-centred concept
The careful introduction of the concept contributes considerably to the reduction of resistance and fear and is likely to motivate and encourage the staff. One way of doing this could include the following three steps:
    1. An informational meeting for the whole staff, where the person-centred concept is presented and discussed. Those staff members who are not yet involved should know too what is planned and get an opportunity to give their opinion.

2. An introducing workshop for the staff of the involved department where, according to its specific needs and conditions, a person-centred concept will be developed and the training given for its transfer into practice.

3. Further training events which will provide the opportunities to reflect, discuss, develop further and, if necessary, modify what has been learned at the workshop and tried out in daily practice.

All the same, if only a part of the organisation works in a person-centred way, conflicts and tensions are inevitable, particularly if the same clients have contact with different departments, such as workshops and residential facilities. The staff has to confront and discuss such difficulties. Clear dividing lines have to be drawn, which are acceptable for the involved departments, and at the same time not too demanding for the clients. In this respect, clear and sensible structures will be a substantial support.

Clear and sensible structures

These are essential for the fluent functioning of an organisation. Here again, limitations and opportunities have to be clearly defined and transparent. In social organisations this is often neglected. There is a tendency for vagueness and confusion, perhaps out of concern to not appear authoritarian. Yet to be clear is definitely not the same as being authoritarian. Patriarchal (or matriarchal)-authoritarian structures are counter-productive for providing living conditions in which people should be able, within their possibilities, to develop. To turn away from authoritarian structures — as has happened in many places but not nearly everywhere yet — is most desirable and even necessary.

But it is as counter-productive to blur or deny existing hierarchies and to pretend they were not there. Even if limited to a minimum, hierarchies exist. To disguise them, as frequently happens in social organisations, merely results in being even more affected by them. Only if the hierarchical structures are clear and transparent can they be dealt with in a constructive and co-operative way. To be able to work in a sensible way, each staff member has to know exactly what are his or her competences and responsibilities. It is amazing how often this is not so at all.

It makes things even more difficult *when structures do not correspond to realities.* Team leading is basically a good idea, especially when taking care of small groups. But it only makes sense if everybody in the team is approximately on the same level of knowledge and experience and to the same degree able to take responsibility.

Example 46

The team of a flat-sharing community consists of two carers plus their replacements for the holidays. The two carers are supposed to equally share, as a team, the position of group manager. However, one of the carers has worked with this group for six years, whereas the second had changed twice during the last year. Very soon, problems arise because the long-term staff member, just by his experience, has a considerable lead over the other, and in practice is the one in charge. Moreover, he is not very motivated to once more, within such a short time, be open to a new person and new ideas. The new carer, on the other hand, wants to assert her leading position, although she is clearly aware that her colleague knows the situation better and that she depends on him to get the necessary information. Both are confused by this ambiguous situation, and tensions and rivalries unnecessarily use up a considerable amount of their energy.

Here a clear structure, appropriate to the real situation, could be worked out as follows: during the first year it is the task of the long-term staff member to manage the group and at the same time to introduce the new carer so that she will get to know and become familiar with the situation. Only after this year will they both manage the group together as a team.

'Team management' often means that it is left to the team to give itself a structure. This asks for *very clear agreements and division of competences among staff members* if they are not to start from silent expectations of each other to stumbling again and again over differing ideas about duties and competences. Sometimes the staff has to *ask the management for clear structures* if they are either not sure or disagree about certain conditions — such as binding hours of contact-time or specific responsibilities.

In order to have a constructive function, structures must not only be clear and adequate to the realities, but also *serve the purpose of the institution.* The purpose of social facilities is to offer the people they accommodate the best possible life conditions. The reality often looks different: priority is on the operational procedure, whereas the well-being of the inhabitants is secondary. Unfortunately the following example has not been invented.

Example 47

Mary and Walt, both over eighty, give up their apartment and move to a (very expensive) private home for older people. There they occupy two rooms which they can furnish with their own furniture. Neither of them needs nursing care. Nevertheless, the rules of this home do not allow them to set up one room as a bedroom and the other as living room. Mary and Walt, after more than fifty years of marriage and sharing the same bedroom, against their will have to accept from now on to sleep in separate rooms.

Facilitating the flow of work and other organisational arrangements do not justify taking away from human beings their entitled right to decide themselves about such personal matters. Structures like these rules contradict the purpose of a home for older people and degenerate into despotic instruments, which unnecessarily make life difficult for the clients. They will for sure, in the end, have negative effects also for the institution itself. Unhappy and discontented inhabitants certainly do not make the staff's life easy.

However, small organisational changes, such as adjustment of work schedules, may considerably help to facilitate work. Maria Schmucki found, and told me that, 'It was the custom on some wards of this nursing home that after 11.30 a.m. there was only one nurse present. For us this represented tremendous stress, because so many things had to be done before 11.30. Finally the schedules were modified, in order to have always two nurses working till noon. This provided a considerable calm down, and we did not need more staff, nor had anybody to work more hours, it just had to be organised differently.'

It is not the issue of this book to design organisational concepts for social institutions. Those examples are to just point to the fact that there is a close connection between the structures of an organisation and the well-being of clients and staff, and to highlight how important it is for structures to be clear and conform to the task.

Consultation and supervision

Working with human beings makes it necessary to question, test and reflect upon what one is doing. This is a demand social organisations have to insist on and provide the adequate instruments for. Yet as much as supervision or consultation is a necessity when working in this field, it is often very difficult to get it accepted. The dilemma is that supervision, as an indispensable part of this work, on the one hand should be made a condition by the institution, but on the other cannot be forced upon the staff against their will, as willingness and motivation to participate in this process are indispensable. Petr Ondracek gives an illustrative picture of how, as a manager of a children's home, he had experienced these difficulties (see Chapter 10 'A children's home in Germany'). Of course, supervision can be ordered and made obligatory, but genuine participation of the staff cannot be enforced. One single person is enough, just through passive resistance, to jeopardise or block the whole process and consequently paralyse the motivation of the other staff members as well.

'Supervision' is not a very comfortable term, as it is used also in the sense of control. Is that why in social organisations fear and resistance concerning supervision is so widespread? To question their work in a constructive way, to recognise problems and to find solutions, professionals do not need control, but accompanying consultation by an outsider. I therefore prefer the term 'practice consultation'. It is more clear and accurate, and at the same time implies that the issue to deal with is professional practice, not personal problems. Of course, those cannot always be strictly separated. Personal problems have an influence on and may get in the way of how somebody is working. Practice consultation is supposed also to make this perspective transparent, but it is not the right setting to work on personal problems. The consultant may point to such connections and perhaps indicate the need, as well as adequate possibilities, of working on these problems, but never should she within the context of practice consultation go into them in detail, let alone 'dig deeper'. The privacy of staff members has to be respected. Unfortunately, this principle is not always respected, which might be another reason why many professionals persistently resist participating in supervision. Yet, supervision or practice consultation should never be threatening, but offer help, support, encouragement and relief. It has to be always in connection with the task to be fulfilled and with difficulties in working together. Practice consultation is not an instrument to deal with personal problems, discords or animosities not related to work.

It is the consultant's responsibility not to lose sight of these conditions and, through the way he works, to build up the necessary foundation for trust. In contrast it is the institution's task to offer an adequate general setting. External consultants have the advantage of another viewpoint and of independence from the hierarchical structures of the organisation. Confidentiality goes without saying, and everybody involved is equally responsible for respecting it.

Supervision or practice consultation is supposed to help the persons involved to accept, for themselves and for each other, that they are not perfect, that mistakes do happen and that nobody is always working the way he would actually like to. Moreover, consulting should convey the experience that such mistakes can be openly discussed and are an opportunity to learn from, to make new experiences and to enlarge a carer's frame of action. Supervision or practice consultation is also a form of permanent education — another reason why it deserves to be carefully encouraged by the institution.

What can an individual carer do?

What can a carer wanting to work in a person-centred way do if the desirable conditions are not present? Is there any chance at all if neither the whole organisation nor the department where he or she works, is based on this concept? Leeway will be small in this case, but is it still possible to adopt person-centred fundamentals even in a limited way.

Under these conditions, what can still be realised is *the basic person-centred attitude.* What we might call the 'respect for the unknown in the other person', the openness for unexpected ways of behaviour and the potential for growth, is still possible, as well as listening to and taking the other person seriously . Even where structures do not leave much space, there may be, here and there, tiny opportunities to let the other person take a decision herself — be it only that she wants to sit at the table or near the window. Even if such approaches will not provoke big changes or establish the desirable continuity, for the time being they are beneficial to those concerned. And sometimes they may radiate and give other staff members new impulses to consider what they are doing and perhaps also the structures within which they work.

Again Maria Schmucki told me, 'It is possible to do something. For example, the custom was that at breakfast everybody got put a roll, jam and butter on their plate. I did not like that. When I was responsible for breakfast, I showed the women the bread basket and let them choose themselves. And I asked, we have this and this jam today, which one would you like? And one day I heard from next door that the colleague on duty did ask too, and with time they all asked. Or when I had to wash a woman and she was still asleep, I let her sleep and went first to her neighbour. At first, the others looked surprised, especially once, when I changed my whole schedule and started to prepare medications instead of waking up the women and wash them. But with time they all found it was good this way and did the same, and nevertheless we all always finished in time.'

So far, we mainly talked about institutions and professionals. The question arises whether the person-centred concept is also useful for families.

8
The person-centred concept and families

Generally speaking, we can say that many problems would not arise at all if some person-centred principles — such as taking the other person seriously, fostering her own way, responding to her experiencing and encouraging her — were followed in raising a child with special needs. Not doing so is the root of many an undesirable development. However, education is not the issue of this book, which deals with questions of care-taking.

A person-centred approach in families may help to make daily routines easier and to cope better with tensions and conflicts. Moreover, this basic attitude allows a relative with special needs, or in need of care, more autonomy and personal freedom, and thus makes things easier for the whole family.

Yet the family situation is different from that of an institution which is (or should be) designed specifically for the well-being of people in need of care. A family setting has to take account of, and offer space for the needs, concerns, sorrows and pleasures of all its members as well as of the one with special needs. *It is the living space of all of them.* In a family, carers are constantly on duty: they do not change according to work schedules, and they cannot quit or go home to regenerate after work. They live at the same place where they carry out their care-taking duties.

Family relationships are not the same as relationships in a social institution. Parents, sisters and brothers are much more involved emotionally with each other — positively as well as negatively. It is harder for them, in difficult situations, to keep some distance. The fact of a person being disabled, ill or impaired has a much stronger emotional impact on her relatives than on those who have to work with her professionally.

People with special needs are often overprotected by their families, which makes it more difficult or even impossible for them to take a step of growth. Most parents have a hard time seeing a son or daughter with special needs as a grown-up person whose own ways should be encouraged. For them, the process of detachment is even more difficult than for parents of 'normal' children. For a family, to find the right balance between giving the care a grown-up disabled person still needs and encouraging their own ways and independence, represents an ongoing challenge. They are so used to having to take care of 'the child' that often they do not realise when the time has come for the adult person to decide himself about certain things. The grown-up son would perhaps like to choose himself which movie he wants to see, instead of just being taken to one by his parents. The adult daughter perhaps no longer enjoys the Sunday routine of visiting her aunt, but would prefer to do something else. People with special needs too, have to be asked what they would like and their wishes have to be taken as seriously as those of 'normal' people — particularly because they sometimes have a hard time expressing them clearly.

Example 48

At a permanent education programme for people with special needs the partcipants learn to express their wishes. Earnest says, 'I don't want anymore, when I come home, for my father to say, "Put on your working clothes, we'll do something in the garden." I want to sit down and read the newspaper.' Earnest cannot read, but obviously for him, settling down after work in an easy chair with the newspaper means enjoying his evening, relaxing and above all doing what other adults (his father, for example) do when they come home from work.

Instead of saying, 'But you can't read!' his wish should be respected. He works all day at the workshop and has a right to enjoy his evenings as he likes. People with special needs too, sometimes feel a need to just do nothing. It is not necessary to keep them permanently busy, out of fear of not caring enough and leaving them to fend for themselves. By doing this, parents stress themselves too, whereas they could benefit as well from allowing the son or daughter a little more autonomy. The principle, 'As much structure as necessary and as much leeway as possible', is also valid within the setting of family life and the person-centred guidelines described in Chapter 4 may be helpful for families too.

Example 49

Bernard (see Example 11) stays at his mother's home for the holidays. He loves to watch television in the evenings at home, because at the institution where he lives there is no opportunity to do so. His mother has to go out for a couple of hours. She is in a hurry and does not want to upset Bernard. Therefore she does not tell him that she is leaving. She knows he will stay in front of the television set unless somebody calls him away. Besides, his younger sister Alma is at home too and she goes to her room in the basement. She does not tell Bernard where she is either, because she knows for sure that he is upstairs watching television and will not move unless he is asked to. But, for some reason, Bernard comes down and finds the living room empty. He goes wild and screams. Hearing him, Alma rushes to the living room. She panics, not knowing how to calm him down. Suddenly she remembers that he likes to take a bath and that this, in the past, had often had a soothing effect on him. So she prepares him a bath, but he resists and struggles even more, splashing water all over the place. Desperately, Alma phones her older sister for help. Together, with great difficulty, they manage to calm Bernard down.

By respecting some of the guidelines described below, this critical situation, or at least its escalation, could have been avoided.

Don't let your guide be what you already know. Bernard's mother knows that Bernard, once he is watching television, does not move until somebody goes and gets him. She acts according to this knowledge, not considering that he could, for once, behave differently.

Clear information. In order to avoid long explanations and the possibility of his protest, she does not tell him that she is going out. Nor does his sister tell him where she is. For Bernard, the situation is not clear at all he just realises that nobody is there and panics. If he had had clear information, he probably would have grumbled at first about his mother leaving, but then come to terms with the situation. And as he had known also where to find his sister, he hardly would have panicked.

Stay with the obvious. Alma is terrified by her brother's tantrum, which she remembers from their childhood. She does not think of the obvious thing that Bernard is upset because he discovers suddenly that his mother is not there. Instead of being empathic, Alma only thinks of how to stop his getting wild. She remembers that a bath sometimes used to calm him down. But he does not want to take a bath; he wants *to be taken seriously,* so he gets even wilder. The situation escalates. If she would have explained to him, 'Mum went out, she will be back soon, I am downstairs in my room,' he would very probably have calmed down soon and gone back to watching television.

On the other hand, as sons or daughters, we often have a hard time accepting that our elderly parents are sometimes confused and say things which cannot be true. It often takes quite some time until we realise it, especially when we have known our father or mother as a strong person with clear thinking. We engage in useless discussions trying to persuade an older person that he is wrong. According to his character and disposition, he will either give in and fall silent or insist even more stubbornly on what he said. It makes more sense for both parties, to either just accept the confused state of mind as it is or to try to grasp its experiencing quality.

Example 50
Alice, who cannot walk anymore, is sitting in her wheelchair next to the window. She points to the garden and tells her daughter: 'I always walk out there, back and forth and back and forth.' It is useless to say, 'That's not true, you cannot walk.' The daughter could just accept it, or try to be empathic with what her mother feels, for example, 'You would like to go for a walk', or, 'You often think of your garden', or perhaps just, 'You always walk back and forth and back and forth'.

As confusion and lucidity sometimes alternate abruptly, it is not always easy for carers to realise on which level an older person is at the moment. The latter is not always quite sure herself if what she is just saying is real or in her imagination. A neighbour who volunteered to take care of an older man for some hours a week had a good image to describe this state of mind.

Example 51
Alfred is very upset and asks the neighbour to drive him immediately to a nearby home for older people where he claims to have stored his carpets. As the neighbour asks questions Alfred is suddenly not quite sure anymore. The carer says: 'At moments we are not quite sure if it is something we dream or if it is something real, right Alfred?' Alfred relaxes and nods. The neighbour had obviously intuitively understood how he felt at the moment.

Perhaps temporary confusion is actually a similar state of mind to that between sleep and awakening, when we are not in our dream anymore, but not quite back to reality yet. Anyway, Alfred felt understood by the carer. The neighbour *took Alfred seriously* and tried to *empathically understand and respond to his experiencing.* This attitude helps a confused older person more than trying to explain to her — mostly in vain — how it really is. Moreover, the wise reaction of the carer, for Alfred's family too, offered a clue to better understanding Alfred and reacting more calmly to his disorientated wishes.

It is certainly not possible, nor even desirable, to design family life along a concept. Yet the examples demonstrate that for families who have to take care of a member with special needs, the person-centred approach offers some helpful guidelines worth trying.

9
Pre-therapy[1]

The concept of pre-therapy developed by the American psychologist Garry Prouty, is one of the most important evolutions of the person-centred approach. Prouty, in a quite impressive way, defeats the frequently raised objection that this approach would not work with severely mentally disabled persons. It is with such clients that Prouty has been remarkably successful with his therapeutic concept. Yet pre-therapy is not only a useful instrument for psychotherapists, but also very helpful in care-taking of so called 'contact-impaired' clients. Pre-therapy is an example of how concretely to realise the person-centred attitude, in dealing with severely disabled persons. Therefore this chapter will give a short summary of this concept.

Pre-therapy makes it possible to approach people who — due to mental disabilities, long-term hospitalisation or mental diseases — are hardly, or not at all, able to be in contact with the world around them, who live withdrawn in themselves and express themselves in 'bizarre' and 'unintelligible' ways, persons who usually are labelled as 'not reachable by therapy' or even 'not capable of contact'.

Prouty's concept of pre-therapy is based on many years of experience with such clients — many of them 'dual diagnosed' as being mentally disabled *and* mentally ill. Pre-therapy is founded on client-centred fundamentals and allows, by carefully listening to, looking at, 'feeling into' and taking seriously the other person, a better understanding of them and their world. Pre-therapy has two possible outcomes:

1. It leads to a genuine psychotherapeutic process where the roots of the isolation or of the hallucination can be reached and traumatic experiences processed and integrated.
2. It does not lead to an actual psychotherapeutic process but to considerable improvements of the client's daily life. Clients are more in contact with the world around them, and more capable of participating in educational and recreational programmes which before had seemed out of reach. Perhaps they can visit more frequently with their families, because they don't raise so much

1 Prouty, 1994; Prouty, Pörtner and Van Werde, 1998.

tension any more. In other words their freedom for action gets enlarged and their life quality improves.

At first Prouty intuitively made contact with these reclusive and hardly accessible persons. Later he began to think about *how* he responded to those clients and to consider methodical and theoretical aspects of his way of working. Prouty uses the expression 'to bridge in', as we need to *build a bridge into the world of the client.* Pre-therapy is a methodical instrument to build such bridges.

The method . . .
. . . is based on *reflections,* aimed at facilitating contact on different levels. *Contact reflections,* as Prouty calls them, embrace five different ways of responding to the client[1].

1. *Situational reflections* (in another form mentioned before in the context of guidelines for everyday work), help to establish *reality contact.* They refer to simple things in the immediate environment: 'We are sitting at the table', 'The lights are on', 'It's hot today', 'The room is big', 'We are both very quiet today', 'You play with the pencil'. These reflections refer to simple things within the client's field of perception.

Example[2]
'Mr X was a 22-year-old paranoid schizophrenic who was very withdrawn, hardly ever speaking to other people. One day the therapist noticed that he was carrying two large batteries in his rear pocket.
He situationally reflected, saying, "You've got two batteries in your pocket."
The client responded by saying that he carried the batteries to help keep "charged contact with girls". By continuing to reflect this delusional material the therapist was able to reach some of the patient's feelings of loneliness.'

2. *Body reflections* aim to *stimulate a person's contact with herself, with her body:* 'you're slumping in your chair', 'you're leaning on your arms', 'your feet are dangling', etc.

Example
'N was a withdrawn, resentful, deeply infantile and regressive retardate who wouldn't function at her work station. Not infrequently, during sessions, she would act out her hostility by seductively sprawling her body on the therapist's desk.

---

2 All the following examples are quoted from Prouty (1976). They have been chosen for their ability to illustrate the method clearly, even if the terminology is a little dated. See also the comments on the use of language p.2.

The therapist responded by body reflecting, saying, "You're lying on my desk . . . You're crawling on the desk".
This body reflecting would heighten her awareness of her seduction, bringing a smile to her face. The therapist could then reflect her smile and carefully try to verbalise the feeling coming with it.'

With people who are not able to respond to verbal communication, it may also be helpful for the therapist to *literally reflect with her body* the client's attitudes or movements. Yet this has to be done very carefully and gently, and it never should be a 'parroting', but a feeling into the posture of the other person in order better to understand how she is feeling.

Example
'T, who was diagnosed alternately as brain damaged and/or schizophrenic, used to come into the therapy room, say nothing and spread himself out like a board on two chairs in a type of catatonic rigidity.
Initially the therapist reflected, saying, "You're lying on the chairs . . . You are stiff and straight."
After several sessions of repeatedly doing this, T would respond by making circular motions with his arms and hands — drawing circles in the air.
The therapist then reflected the motions of his arms and hands by copying with his arms and hands and by saying repeatedly, "You're making circles in the air with your arms."
T at last began to emit word-like utterances which the therapist then could reflect.'

3. *Facial reflections* stimulate a person's *contact with her own feelings,* for example, 'You seem sad', 'You're frowning', 'You're smiling'. Many times mentally disabled or psychotic persons feel something, but out of fear or resignation or because of lack of confidence, do not dare to express it. Sometimes they cannot even recognise their feelings as something belonging to themselves. To reflect their facial expression may facilitate the contact with their feelings and at the same time make them experience that their feelings are a perceivable human experience in which another person can participate.

Example
'B was a retarded schizophrenic, mostly non-verbal, who had never shown any feeling with the therapist. One day the client brought a newspaper clipping illustrating an elephant that had escaped from the local zoo. The client didn't speak verbally, but smiled happily about the clipping.
Responding to the smile, the therapist reflected the happy feeling in the youngster's face saying, 'You're happy about the elephant,' and

"You like animals."
The response was a very solid head nodding, and the therapist knew the youngster had learned she was someone to have feeling with.'

4. *Word for word reflections* establish contact with others and are particularly useful with persons who have language difficulties. Perhaps they just utter a jumble of nearly inaudible, incoherent or unintelligible scraps of words or sounds where an understandable word or a coherent sentence emerges only sporadically. In this context there are two possibilities for word for word reflections:
i) the therapist reflects the occasional words or sounds that are understandable and coherent, or
ii) the therapist literally reflects sounds or words that are not understandable but obviously have more emotional content.

For people who desperately try to express themselves, it means a lot to experience that somebody responds at all, that they are not just ignored. In addition, by reflecting word for word, the therapist uses the same images the client herself uses and understands. This way the client experiences that the therapist grasps what she tries to express. Thus communication develops.

Example
'Z was a retardate schizophrenic, struggling with an hallucination which deeply frightened him. A word for word segment follows:
Z: "I'm scared."
T: "You're scared."
Z: "I'm scared."
T: "You're scared."
Z: "I'm scared."
T: "You're scared."
Z: "I am frightened."
T: "You are frightened."
Z: "I really am frightened."
T: "You really are frightened."
Z: "Yes, boy, this is really real."
By reflecting word for word and precise word shifts, every nuance of feeling is experienced and expanded.'

5. *The reiterative principle* stimulates the client's feelings anew and helps him to remember them and sort them out. The reiterative principle consists in coming back to those reflections which had created contact and repeating them several times. Thus the client's experiencing is stimulated anew and may grow further. The client's faculties for contact are different from day to day. Therefore it makes sense to come back to former contact moments, in order to pick up the connection, to stimulate

the process of communication and to foster 'ongoingness'.

Example

'Two weeks ago the client smiled when the therapist reflected her head rocking. The therapist may have to repeat this until there will be again a reaction.

Or:

The client may only be able to express a few words, and it may be necessary for the therapist to go back to these words again and again in order to maintain contact. This may amount to patiently and persistently, perhaps for weeks, repeating and re-sharing the same place where something had been expressed or was about to be expressed.'

These contact reflections may, at first sight, appear quite simple. Yet they would fail to work if we tried to use them just mechanically as a technique. The examples make it clear that they require patience, empathy and taking the client seriously. *'The principle is simple, but the art is difficult',* is Prouty's comment. He emphasises that pre-therapy is not a set of mechanically applicable techniques, but a method based on a solid person-centred attitude, on the willingness to enter the world of the clients and to go gently and *in their rhythm* with their, perhaps just tiny, steps of growth.

The purpose of contact reflections is *to enable the clients' contact with reality, with themselves and with others.* Chronic schizophrenic, long-term hospitalised patients as well as severely mentally disabled persons live in a secluded, autistic world, hardly accessible or understandable for others. The same is true for persons in an acute psychotic episode. The difference is that in a psychosis people lose contact with reality, whereas severely mentally disabled persons often could not develop contact, or only in a very limited way. With psychotic patients contact has to be restored, whereas with severely mentally disabled persons contact has to be established.

Working with hallucinations

Garry Prouty believes, and his clinical experience proves, that in the root of every hallucination, of every autistic or bizarre behaviour, there are real traumatic experiences. In working with people with special needs, he found that alarmingly often there was an incest problem in the family. Usually in these cases, the family had vehemently opposed the therapy.

Instead of regressive, Prouty uses the term *pre-expressive.* It implies that there is something clients *cannot yet express.* In order to help them, step by step, to become able to express it, Prouty, very carefully and concretely, stays with what *they*, verbally or non-verbally, communicate and with *their* images.

Example

'The client, a 19-year-old male who had gone through some therapy as described before, began to relate about:

"Something that was there, and probably always was there."

After using very careful facial and word for word reflections, gradually the phenomenology of a hallucination began to emerge. Tape recorded descriptions report the client experienced:

"a picture with feelings in it — like a painting only with feelings in it"

"big, purple, orange and yellow."

With gentle acceptance by the therapist and continued verbal reiteration of the structure and emotional content of the hallucination (size, colour, shape, feelings), the hallucination changed into:

"purple, terrorizing, demonic, laughing, cruelty, with considerable hate in it."

With weeks of patient reiteration, structure and feeling processed into:

"an orange square with anger in it."

Additional weeks of structural and feeling reiteration, and the hallucination evolved into a:

"woman with orange hair — who looks pretty mean."

Finally, with persistent reiteration of image, structure and feelings, the orange-haired woman processed into a nun school teacher who had beaten the youngster with a yard-stick. At this time the hallucination process ceased. By reflecting the structural-phenomenological properties and associated feelings, the hallucination was experientially processed back to its early trauma. The described therapy process happened within about 18 months.'

Prouty persistently stays with the phenomenon, with the image, the shape and the colour of the hallucination. The spatial dimension of the hallucination is another meaningful aspect he carefully pays attention to. Hallucinations have to be seen as a part of the client's reality and taken seriously. If this does not happen, the client will be more and more cut off from his emotional process.

Prouty describes hallucinations as *pre-symbolic*. The image is there, yet its meaning cannot be understood, whether by the therapist or by the client. Therapy here means going with the client step by step into this scary place until the symbolic meaning reveals itself and the traumatic experience becomes visible. Then the experience has to be carefully integrated into the self. To follow the client in this process, as far as into the abyss, is highly demanding for a therapist. It requires not only professional skills, but the whole person.

Of course, it is not always, or even very rarely, possible to reveal the meaning of hallucination or to penetrate to the core of isolation. But to approach a client not as 'mad', but as a person whose strange behaviour for her has a meaning and symbolises concrete experiences, though we cannot understand it, has in itself a therapeutic value. This is true not only for the therapy session, but also in daily life.

Applications in daily life

It is important for Garry Prouty to make known his approach to staff working in different areas of psychiatric hospitals and institutions for people with special needs. In Ghent, Belgium, for example, the psychologist Dion Van Werde runs a ward of a psychiatric hospital entirely based on the concept of pre-therapy (see Chapter 9). In the US, some years ago, Garry Prouty had initiated a two-year training programme for 'para-professionals', as he called it. These people were taught to try in everyday situations to stimulate the clients' contact functions in the described way.

For example, on the way to the shower a facilitator may say: 'We walk through the hall. I open the door. You undress. The water is warm. You splash the water. You laugh.' Or the accompanying person on a walk: 'We walk side by side. We take big steps. You hold my arm' etc. One of Prouty's students created a game with contact reflections as a recreation activity for children with special needs. Its purpose was to provide fun for the children, but at the same time, in a playful way, to foster their contact functions.

There are many other possibilities to imagine how contact reflections could be used in daily life, for example, with confused older people. There is freedom for carers' creativity, on condition, however, that any form of application is based on an attitude of empathy, acceptance and congruence and never appears disrespectful. Applications in daily life are aimed *at developing and reinforcing the clients' contact functions*, not criticising their behaviour.

The effects of Prouty's pre-therapy have been proved in several empirical research projects and described in various publications[3]. Prouty's approach has spread to Europe. Particularly in Belgium, where two psychiatric hospitals, for ten years now, have pre-therapy programmes going on, it has considerably developed[4]. Pre-therapy has been taken up also in Italy and the Netherlands, as well as in Germany where

---

3   See references
4   Prouty, Pörtner and Van Werde, 1998.

since 1992 Prouty has taught several seminars, and where recently some institutions have begun to integrate pre-therapy. In September 1995 the Pre-therapy International Network, based in Ghent, was founded, with the purpose to facilitate exchange and co-ordination between the different countries and to develop a consistent training concept.

10
The person-centred approach in different professional fields

Included here are three examples from different countries and different professional fields which will demonstrate how person-centred fundamentals can be transferred into different fields, and stimulate readers to think about how, in their own field of activity, a person-centred way of working could be realised.

A psychiatric ward in Belgium

At the psychiatric hospital 'Kliniek Saint-Camillus' in Ghent, the psychologist Dion Van Werde[1] has set up a ward entirely based on pre-therapeutic principles. It is an open ward which admits up to twenty patients with different forms of psychotic disorders, on condition that they are capable of coping with an open ward (not acutely suicidal, for example, or constantly running away), to participate to some degree in the ward activities (for example the weekly ward meeting) and to take over minor duties.

Van Werde defines the way they work on this ward as 'person-centred and reality-oriented'. Nurses try to be empathic with the patients' experiencing instead of interpreting or judging their behaviour. The central issue is to restore and reinforce contact. Stimulating and fostering the patients' contact functions is not left to the psychologist, nor limited to therapy hours, but sets the tone of the ward's daily life. Van Werde works from the fact that nurses are around patients day and night and thus have innumerable contact points to pick up. Nurses use contact reflections as a helpful way to meet patients in *their* world and to establish contact. Even the cleaning team is encouraged to stimulate contact by not just silently doing their work, but telling the patients what they are doing, for example: 'I have to wipe the floor now.' This also may contribute to help patients to get into contact with the immediate reality around them.

---

1 Prouty, Pörtner and Van Werde, 1998.

Prouty did several seminars at the clinic and the staff got a basic training in principles of pre-therapy. Van Werde helped to deepen and develop the staff's knowledge by advising and supporting them in how to transfer the concept into the ward's daily life.

The nurses try, wherever it is possible and not interfering with their responsibilities for the ward as a whole, to reflect psychotic behaviour of the patients. This means that nurses respond to the patients as much as possible, but at the same time accept and take into account, as part of reality, the rules and circumstances of the ward. 'In everyday ward-life, we continuously try to make the bridge between these two fields of interest. For example, yelling or laying down on the floor can be very meaningful within someone's psychotherapeutic process, but incompatible with the house-rules of the ward. A bridge then could be first to reflect the yelling and e.g. the facial expressions that go with it, and then to limit or stop the yelling, whenever it is too loud and too disturbing for the other patients of the ward.'[2] Such 'bridges' meet one of the essential imperatives of the person-centred concept described above of finding an adequate balance between structure and freedom (see p.13).

The following is an example of the use of contact reflections in an everyday situtation:[3]

'Christiane walks into the nurses' office, stands still and stares straight ahead. She is obviously in a kind of closed, locked-up position, but nevertheless she has come to the office or to the nurses. Instead of immediately telling her to go back to her room or instructing her first to knock on the door and then come in, one of the nurses empathically reflects what is happening, "You are standing in the office," (situational reflection); "You look in the direction of the window," (situational reflection); "You are staring," (facial reflection). These reflections seem to enable Christiane to contact her feelings and free herself from whatever had been on her mind in a way that she could not master. She now says, "I am afraid that my mother is going to die!" Then she turns around and walks towards the living room. The semi-psychotic mood is processed and she is once again in control of herself. She thus becomes able to feel and to communicate in a congruent way and does not ask for further attention. She can take care of herself once again even though the intervention is short and technically simple.'

By empathically reflecting the situation and the facial expression a piece of 'normality' is established and further escalation avoided. 'We

2 Van Werde, 1993; 1995.
3 Van Werde, 1994.

react quite normally, also to bizarre elements', Dion Van Werde said in a conversation we had together — corresponding to the principle 'go from the normal situation' I described in the 'guidelines for everyday work' (see Chapter 4).

'To be in contact means to limit psychosis', says Van Werde, 'and to realise, "Today I am sad," means to perceive, "I am not totally psychotic, I am also sad."' In order to be in contact, we need to perceive. Therefore, on the ward, they try toreinforce the patients' sense of perception in various ways and on different levels.

For example, in a group meeting, the patients were asked to say which noises they heard. They named birds singing in the park, traffic on the road, steps in the corridor, the clatter of dishes, 'the voice of my father'. The team responds to that; suddenly a patient hears his father's voice, which the others don't hear, but that he also hears the traffic noises which the others do hear. This difference is pointed to: there is a common reality and an individual reality. The patient has perceived both, his inner voice and the traffic noise. This means he is not *just* psychotic, he also perceives real noises. It is very important for Van Werde to encourage the strong and healthy parts in a person. If patients feel more grounded, more anchored, they will better come to terms with their psychotic parts. Van Werde compares their condition with a tree, which has a big and rampant crown, but only very weak roots. 'We have to work on the roots, not basically cut the crown, or always just work on the crown,' says Van Werde. It is a beautiful image to illustrate the person-centred assumption that any delusion, any behaviour, as 'crazy' as it might be, for the involved person has a meaning, in the sense of Prouty's notion of 'pre-expressive' (see p.82). The point is not to eliminate it by therapy but, together with the patient, to try to approach its meaning and to find other and better ways to live with it.

The weekly ward meeting for patients and staff, chaired by Van Werde, is an integral part of ward life. It takes place every Thursday, and those staff members working the following weekend are present, in order to know what is going on and what the patients are preoccupied with. The meeting serves several purposes: patients get an opportunity to express their concerns, the leisure programme which the patients organise themselves is discussed, agreements are made concerning who will take over which duties for the next week. Staff members express their concerns too and share information. So far this meeting is not different from those held in other hospitals. What is so special about it, again, is the focus. 'The running thread through the weekly ward meeting is the restoration and consolidation of the contact functions.' [4]

Van Werde always opens the meeting with the remark: 'Today is Thursday, such an such a date, the time is 15.45, this is our ward-meeting which will last 45 minutes till 16.30. We are here to talk with each other. We may talk about many things, the weather, the programmes provided by the hospital, current events, housework. If you have something too personal or private for this setting, please talk it through with your therapist, with a nurse or with your psychiatrist.' This introduction is meant to support the patients' orientation in time and to encourage them to get into contact with each other, but also to make it very clear that this meeting is not group therapy and that nobody should feel pressured to make personal confessions.

If necessary and possible, the staff responds with contact reflections to a patient's behaviour. For example, 'Chantal suddenly stands up, points at the window and says, "I see them moving again." I reflect word for word and also the anxious expression of her face. This intervention seems to anchor her. She looks around, becomes aware of the group again and we all can continue with the meeting. The group is relieved that she's with us again and that a possible psychotic episode doesn't automatically lead to repressive interaction, but instead is dealt with in a very accepting and containing way.' (ibid)

The reality of the world around is also referred to, for example: 'Today is All Souls' Day.' Such references may help to further develop and strengthen the newly established contact functions. Perhaps somebody will remember a relative who died, and realise: 'I am sad.' This feeling is reflected, but — within the setting of the ward meeting — not in order to work therapeutically on it, but to communicate to the patient that her feelings are perceived and understood. Perhaps others have similar feelings. If patients can mutually perceive that in each other, there is contact. Or one of the staff members reminds: 'Tomorrow is a holiday in the German speaking part of Belgium.' Perhaps some patients realise, for the first time, that there is a German speaking population in Belgium, and ask questions, or a patient remembers friends who live in this area. All these are clues for reality contact.

Sometimes particularly motivated nurses take over special projects with a patient or a small group of patients. Or trainees do a project as part of their training. For example, a trainee tries to develop a training programme for a young man who has no orientation in time, is always late and therefore misses most of the activities. She hangs a big clock on the wall and a coloured day schedule. In the morning she discusses with him, step by step, what will go on. He participates and seems to

4 Van Werde, 1993; 1995.

understand. But as soon as she has left the room, he forgets everything and again is late everywhere. 'As long as somebody has no contact with himself, training programmes don't work', is Van Werde's comment. However, he has noticed that the young man is greeting the trainee when he meets her in the corridor, which he never does with other people. It had not been possible to train a specific skill, but on a much deeper level a human relationship is coming into being. That's exactly where Van Werde sees a moment of contact for the trainee to pick up. Or a nurse has planted tulips with the patients. Every week they go and see how the tulips have grown. They notice for example, 'Last week we didn't see anything. Now there is this tiny green tip coming out.'

Another project[5] tried to support the 'cultural anchoring' of the patients. The living room got decorated with different insignia of Flemish identity, flags, posters, pictures of well-known buildings and of Flemish athletes, typical articles of daily life etc. This was meant not only to do something to prevent the anonymity of the hospital, but also to stimulate the patients to remember their Flemish identity, whether by their interest for sports or by any other point of reference. All these are opportunities to stimulate, on various levels, the patients' reality contact in a casual way and without pressure.

One of the occupational therapists too decided to comment less on the objects the patients are working on — 'This is coming along nicely', 'When will you have it finished?' etc. — and to respond more to the patients themselves and on the level they are at the moment: 'You draw with a yellow pencil' (situational reflection) or, 'Yesterday you drew a face' (reiterating reflection), 'Today you draw a face' (situational reflection) or, 'You say it is terrible for you to sit here' (word for word reflection), 'Today you look sad' (facial reflection) etc. This way the patient is given space for the way she feels and contact may develop, with the material as well as with the therapist. This helps her to make a small step out of her autistic isolation[6].

At the beginning, Van Werde's work conditions at the hospital were far from ideal. The importance his work was given was not clear at all: sometimes he felt more tolerated than supported. However, as long as the ward did not attract attention, he was relatively free, although nothing out of the ordinary was tolerated. The sign 'Contact' Van Werde had posted on the ward door had to be taken away, a ward with its own name was not welcome. In the meantime the importance of Van

5 Van Werde and Van Akoleyen, 1994.
6 Mulkers and Van Werde, unpublished manuscript.

Werde's work is increasingly acknowledged. The hospital realises with satisfaction that visitors from abroad show interest in the ward concept and they are warmly welcomed. Van Werde concedes, 'Perhaps what I took for tolerance implies more support than I thought, it's just not so obvious. Yet, it conforms to the philosophy of the nuns who run the hospital, to keep a low profile and just work without talking a lot about it.'

The support of the hospital has become more obvious since in 1998 it became the domicile of the International Pre-Therapy Training Institute and hosts the events of the Pre-Therapy Network. For many years, Van Werde had practically no influence on the selection of new staff members, so that what had been achieved could be seriously endangered by changes in the staff, but this has now changed. He still depends on the psychiatrists to actively support his work — which to different degrees, but increasingly, they do. What Van Werde achieved under the circumstances has to be highly valued. It is an encouraging example of how an individual can effect change in an institution. 'We have to be empathic also with the system, then a lot is possible,' is Dion Van Werde's conviction.

A children's home in Germany

Petr Ondracek, now a professor in special education in Bochum, in the 1980s had been director of a home for sixty children and adolescents. His job was to update the institution's old-fashioned structures. Looking back on a long tradition, the home had been destroyed by bombs during World War II and rebuilt after the war. On re-opening it had to take care mainly of war orphans, and later of children with behavioural and developmental disorders or from a diffcult family background. In the early 1980s the home still worked on a concept conceived for the post-war years, centrally organised and aimed at keeping any strain away from, and taking complete care of, the 'poor children' who had suffered so much during the war. This no longer reflected modern times or up-to-date theories about child-rearing and did not meet the requirements of the authorities which had placed the young people.

Ondracek wanted to contribute his person-centred orientation to this work. 'With this I sometimes fell flat on my face or bumped into limits, but I also achieved something,' he says, looking back. When he failed it had much to do with the fact that the person-centred training programmes he had followed did not sufficiently underline the different contexts of psychotherapy and other professional fields. This led him to look at everything from a therapeutic point of view and to make the false assumption that there were no boundaries, which soon caused him problems. His failures showed him the boundaries and taught him that the effectiveness of the person-centred attitude depends on the situational context. Ondracek recognised, 'There are boundaries whithin myself, which I can work on, but there are real boundaries too, which I have to respect.' His experience proves, once more, how in person-centred work it is imperative to clearly acknowledge, and take into account, the general setting of a situation. This, for Petr Ondracek, became clear very soon when working in practice.

What does being person-centred mean for Petr Ondracek? 'For me person-centred means, first of all, orientation: to orientate in myself, in the other person and in our common context, and to enable the other person to orientate herself in a similar way. For that I have to open up and to not deny, but consider the situational context. This is my responsibility in non-therapeutic professional fields. The point here is to recognise and use the growth potential in daily life. The person-centred attitude can open a space for growth and new experiences. It is an accepting attitude, not demanding but offering, which can admit that the other person may say no and not be interested in co-operation. And there we have the first limit already; if the other person refuses to co-operate, I am stuck. Children whose behaviour does not conform to the norms of our expectations, are often not willing to cooperate. Staff members sometimes too, feel unsure about a boss who tries to involve them, and suspect that there must be a catch to it. It is not easy to dissolve those limits. To dissolve them means to coming to agreement and accepting each other so that we can co-operate for the task we have to fulfil. That's what we are here and paid for, to foster and stabilise these children's growth process, and it will work better if we co-operate than if we don't.'

The details of the neccessary restructuring were not to be decided over the heads of those concerned but together with them it was approached as a problem to be discussed and considered. Yet, some of the children and adolescents, as well as some staff members, were deeply afraid of any kind of change. This had a paralysing effect which made it difficult to win them over for active participation. Then some things just had to have decisions made about them, like closing the large kitchen and having the groups preparing their meals themselves. Actually, this had been the staff's wish, but then they got scared of taking over the responsibility. So I had to order that this change should be tried, first for a year, and then be considered again and decided on how to go on. This way the staff had the possibility to experience the change step by step, to consider its advantages and disadvantages and, if they wanted, to continue to participate in the decision-making process.

Another decision had to be made in order to provide steady relationships. In some of the groups the staff should no longer work shifts, but live with the children. At that time this was seen as an educational 'must' , the staff could not participate in this particular decision, but they got detailed information on what was planned and why. They were given time to think it over and the opportunity to be the first ones to apply for work in these groups. Only those who did not want to work on these conditions, were replaced by new staff. This way four groups, based on the new concept, could be set up from their own ranks. (Two of these groups still exist to this day.)

Petr Ondracek, in his position as director of the home, did not consider control, but co-operation and consultation as the first priorities. He discussed with the staff what was going on, what the problems and implications were, and the additional support necessary. Transparency was essential for him, not in order to impose sanctions, but to find out how something came about and what could possibly be done differently. 'We should not, in an irresponsible way, let mistakes pass, but we have to accept that mistakes are made. In this work, again and again, there are situations we have no general rule for. Not surprisingly there was a high percentage of ways of working that did not conform to what was required. What I wanted, was to win people over to learn from the daily events, to grow, to leave familiar paths and make new experiences. Here too, there are limits we have to be aware off. Like anything else in the world, this free structure can be misused, for example by the staff to manipulate or outwit each other. If something like that happened, this created a similar situation for the children as what they had known in their family, so they could not make new experiences. This, very clearly contradicted our task. When I realised that the task was no longer first priority, I had to point to it. I needed to constantly pay attention, not by controlling, but by being perceptive and empathic, also to the situation, in order to be able to intervene in time if necessary. Actually, I was not paid for ignoring the boundaries, but for working with them. It is a kind of pulsating between freeplay and confronting boundaries.'

Also in terms of working with the children, Petr Ondracek considers the person-centred approach as valuable and helpful. He gives an example to illustrate this:

'The four-year-old Cathy, at home, had been very spoiled and dominated the family. This was different at the children's home where she was not all the time the most important child. Other children too drew attention. To some degree she could solve that by her being small. During the morning she used to sneak away from the group and visit people in the offices, this way getting the attention she was looking for. She came to my office too. If I was busy, I first reflected her need for attention, "You would like me to be with you right now,"and then told her how I felt, "I like you and I would like to be with you for a while, but . . ." (this was the context of the situation) "right now I can't. You have to go back to the group, you cannot stay here. When I am finished, I will come to see you upstairs for ten minutes, and we can do something together." This worked. Though she was not very happy with it, the situation for her was clear. I recognised what she wanted, and did not reprimand, but accept it. She experienced that I did not reject her wish, but that, in the actual situation, it could not be met. Moreover it was not completely refused, I offered her something which at the same time I limited to ten minutes. This helped Cathy not to make a big fuss, which usually was the next step of her manipulative behaviour. When she came to the office and the staff had a meeting or a phone call, they told her, "You are disturbing, please go away." Then she made a fuss, threw herself on the floor, had to be carried to her room. She got punished, the situation escalated. And Cathy got what she wanted. The staff did not realise that this way she got her attention, even if, for everybody, in an straining and unpleasant way.

The example shows how in daily life of an educational insitution, the person-centred attitude may help to diminish negative interactions. To handle a situation this way again leads to getting orientated on three levels: in myself, in the other, in the situational context, and then I am in a position to act. The children too, this way get a chance to adjust and behave differently from their usual pattern. They can make a new experience.'

Ondracek liked to help out working in a group when they were short of people. He did it frequently and always enjoyed it, 'Probably because I did not have to work there every day;' he openly admits.'In daily routine, staff members often get insensitive to the beautiful aspects of this work'. And he gives another example:

'Once, I took over the evening shift of a staff member who was ill. At the end of a day, I usually feel the need to experience community in a sense of, "It's good that you are here and good for me to be here". I said that, again, not as a demand, but as an offer and as my personal concern. Dinner at the groups was often like a tug-of-war, the children wanted the meal to be as short as possible, they came late or pushed off quickly. My statement had not the effect that the children were particularly quiet, but that they stayed. We did not eat too quickly, we talked, it was cosy, it was a community situation. And after dinner it became not too hectic either, the children did no longer feel drawn to rush outside, there was a nice atmosphere in the group. When it was time to go to bed, I clearly asked them to do so, without letting myself into discussions. Very soon they were quiet. The next day, the educator on duty reported how at breakfast the children had told him how nice the previous evening had been. For me, this confirmed that, with our attitude, we can considerably contribute in creating a better atmosphere for almost everybody. But it cannot be enforced. I opened up, communicated my need and waited to see what it would lead to. I offered a space to do something together in order to meet this need. This way, even in daily routine, we can create nice moments. It could as well have been different, my need might not have been in tune with their needs, then we would have had to handle the situation differently. It is, again, a matter of orientation. I don't mean that it absolutely has to go my way. But I have the courage to say, "This is me, this is important for me," and if it does not work, I know where I stand and can adjust to the situation. And for the children it would be quite different if I was trying to impose a rule on them disguised as my wishes. Children have a nose for weak points, they sense it when somebody is hiding, and then they start to press.'

How could Ondracek motivate the staff, the majority of which had another professional orientation, to work with a person-centred attitude? Above all, Ondracek relied on continuing education, on supervision and on encouraging new experiences. But it was not easy to win them over. Though Ondracek is convinced: 'There are possibilities to deal with daily routine in education in a way that diminishes stress. Yet, people have to be able to reflect what's going on, to orientate themselves and recognise their own parts in it. However, this caused anxieties and fears of making mistakes and they had to be transformed into the insight, "I cannot be totally okay all the time, again and again there are situations or moments, when it does not go the way I would like." It was a situation not everybody could cope with. Yet, sometimes a crisis helped people to accept supervision. Perhaps I also achieved something by setting an example myself. Some of the staff were willing to take those steps. It worked well and improved their orientation and capacity to act. Others were too scared and could not be motivated. Then I had to speak up clearly because, as a professional and director, I was responsible for things moving on. And if the staff could contribute by looking into themselves, I had to insist that they did so.'

Getting this through, Petr Ondracek felt, was one of the most difficult tasks during his time as director of this home. As much as possible he tried to do it in a person-centred way. He offered opportunities for discussion, organised case work and conferences, where they investigated in detail what had been going on with the different children during the year. What had become of the goals they had set? Why had this one been achieved and another had not? What was neccessary now? Those questions often resulted in staff members' insight that they had to handle the situation differently. Yet it was a long and diffcult way to transfer this insight into action. So many things had become a rigid habit. But Ondracek definitely holds the opinion that daily life at the home had to be shaped in a way to stabilise the children in their developmental process and allow them to have new experiences. If this was endangered, he set clear conditions — either the concerned staff members were ready for supervision and consulting, in order to improve their professional know-how, or they had to be replaced.

Ondracek, at first, had a hard time with this clearness. It contradicted his need to work in a person-centred way. Yet he learned from experience that this cannot be done indefinitely, but has its limits where the essential issues are endangered. Person-centred work has to acknowledge the general setting of the institution and focus on its task. 'The home is there for the children, not for the staff's therapy,' Petr Ondracek concludes.

The example shows that on the organisational level as well as in the work itself, there is space to work in a person-centred way, on condition that the structure or, as Ondracek puts it, the situational context, is clearly recognised and taken into account.

Community work in South Africa[7]
Rini Schenck worked at the Department of Social Work at the University of South Africa in Pretoria, where she participated in community development projects for black communities. She found that in this work, where different cultural concepts collided, it was virtually a must to work in a person-centred way because otherwise often, over the heads of the people they were intended for, projects were carried out that did not really meet their needs. She illustrated this by the following example.
  'After the elections which ended apartheid, the workers of a diamond mine could get their families to live with them. A big multistoried house was placed at their disposal on the grounds of the mine. "From my, white, point of view it was a very comfortable and beautiful house," Rini Schenck underlines. But the black mine workers and their families did not want to move in. Instead they built, on fallow land nearby, makeshift huts of corrugated iron and planks. The big

7 This section is based on an oral report Rini Schenck gave at the Sixth International Forum on the Person-Centred Approach at Leptokaria (Greece) in July 1995.

house they only used to get water. The huts had neither electricity, nor water, nor a sewage system. The hygienic conditions were disastrous. The settlement was a slum which, with each rain, got drowned by mud.

Inevitably this raised comments like, "You can see how primitive the blacks are, they don't even care for better conditions." Yet, Rini Schenk and her team, who had been put in charge of motivating the inhabitants of the slum to move to the house, came to quite different conclusions. In-depth conversations revealed that it was unthinkable, for these people who had grown up in rural communities, to live on top of each other in one big house. What they needed, was a hut for each family, on ground level, with a bit of land around it and connected by footpaths, so that they easily could go to see each other. For them, this was more important than water or electricity, though they did not at all refuse such conveniences. It would have been of no use to force these people to move to the house. Instead, the social workers proposed that the company should place at their disposal the necessary material to build more solid dwellings, provide the settlement with electricity, water and a sewage system and surface the paths so that they would remain passable during the rains. As the land belonged to the mine, it was no problem to do this. Moreover, it was a solution at reasonable costs and which satisified the people concerned.'

It would have been even more reasonable to ask people earlier and let them participate in the planning. This is the way Rini Schenk and her team work with all the projects they are in charge of right from the start, as in this example.

'Within the context of a community development project, the women of a settlement had asked for a day nursery. Instead of just providing it without further inquiry, the team first discussed in detail with the women why they wanted this, what exactly they had in mind and what their expectations were. It turned out that they wished to work and contribute to the family income. This wish was realistic as there were enough opportunities to get work in this area. They then discussed if a day nursery would really meet these needs best, or if there were perhaps elder women in the community, grandmothers, aunts etc., who could take care of the children during work hours and would like to take over this task. A bus trip was organised for the women to visit existing day nurseries in the area, as well as a village where the elder women of the community took care of the children. They could then form an impression and be in a better position to decide which solution was best for them.'

This is a nice example for what in my concept I call 'looking for the concrete' (see p.40). The women were not just provided with a day nursery, which they might have had a wrong idea about and later been disappointed. Together with them the task force tried to find out what they really wanted and needed. Did they really need a day nursery, or were there other options which would meet their needs better? This way confusions on both sides can be, as far as possible, avoided. At the same time, by encouraging people to find their own solutions, their autonomy is fostered. The decision-making process is an opportunity to learn something as well as to develop self-esteem. For the women in our example, it was the first time they went on a bus trip together, their first excursion beyond the immediate neighbourhood — this in itself was an exciting event and a new experience.

The following example too is quite revealing:
'A patron intended to sponsor water pipes to connect a commmunity to the water system. Up to then the women had to walk about a mile to a well to get water. In this case too, before starting to carry out the project, people were asked for their opinion. The men were for the project, but, to everybody's surprise, the women were against it. Why? For them, to walk to the well was an opportunity to meet and to chat without the men being present. This, they did not want to give up. Interestingly enough, the meeting attached more importance to the women's desire than to the men's consent. The community, for the time being, decided to do without the water pipes.'

Here, a next step could be to find out together if other opportunities could be found for the women to have their chat, undisturbed by the men, and if the water pipes could be built once this need was met.

Rini Schenck described how diffcult it was sometimes to convince well-meaning donors not to just sponsor a fountain or a building (which if possible should bear their name) but first to discuss the idea with those concerned whether the gift was really welcome or if something quite different might be needed — something which perhaps afterwards could not so easily be identified as donation of a particular person or organisation. Schenck emphasised the importance of not just showering the, up to then, underprivileged black population with welfare conforming to white ideas, but of making it possible for them to find out themselves what they really needed and to participate with their own ideas in improvements needing to be done.

Of course, not every desire, not every idea of Utopia, could be granted. The taskforce's competences and financial means were limited. But within this framework these people living in the communities could decide for themselves what was most important. The social workers' task was to go with and help to clarify the decision making process. It was a fascinating new experience for everybody. Again, it was a matter of finding an adequate balance between structure and freedom, which as mentioned before, is one of the principles of the person-centred concept.

The three examples from different professional fields conform to a large degree to the principles and guidelines described earlier. They may give an idea of how the person-centred approach is valuable for, and can be adapted to, many different working contexts. These different situations can of course include long-stay institutions (of which there are progressively fewer in the UK), residential homes for the elderly and state schools experiencing problems with disruptive pupils, to name a few.

11
Similar approaches in nursing

Nursing is no longer seen today as an auxiliary medical job depending on doctors, but as an independent profession with specific tasks and competences. In the last decades approaches have been developed which point in a similar direction as the person-centred concept and work, in part, from the same fundamentals.

Humanistic nursing concepts
During the 1960s and 1970s, nursing was given fresh impulses by humanistic psychology which were particularly picked up in Anglo-Saxon countries. It became more and more obvious that bio-medical models alone did not sufficiently meet the demands of nursing.

Paterson and Zderad designed a humanistic nursing concept which viewed nursing as 'an experience between human beings'.[1] To this day, the humanistic nursing concepts fall back on this basic work. They refer, among other things, to Rogers and to a phenomenological view. The following statement may illustrate the relation to the person-centred approach:

'A humanistic nursing concept views each human being as a unique person who, by her experience and biography, is in a position to judge her physical condition and to estimate its meaning whithin the context of her life. She is able to deal with the situation and, with the help of the nurses, make the necessary decisions to either restore her health or make her condition tolerable.'[2]

In humanistic nursing concepts the patients' *experiencing* is of crucial importance. 'How does a patient experience his illness and his health, what effects does the illness have on his daily life and how does he integrate it? These are questions nurses have to ask. They may get their orientation from general tendencies, but how it is for this specific person, they can only learn from herself,' Harry Hulskers specifies in our interview.

---

1 Paterson and Zderad (1976), quoted in Käppeli (1990).
2 Gogl and Stadelmann-Buser (1993).

In 1990 Silvia Käppeli developed an *integrated nursing concept* taking into account bio-medical, as well as social-humanistic, aspects of nursing.[3] This holistic concept claims that nursing has to deal with the patients' objective suffering, as well as with their subjective suffering. It shows perspectives for adequate caring, also of older and chronically ill patients, for whom medicine is no longer effective. Just as in the person-centred concept, it is a matter of looking for the patients' resources and not just concentrating on their deficiencies. With life-threatening and acute diseases the bio-medical aspects are predominant, whereas with older or chronically ill patients, humanistic aspects are much more important.

As long as nursing is seen exclusively from a medical point of view, caring for the old or chronically ill patients will not enjoy much prestige and be left to less qualified staff. Though it is true that this kind of nursing does not need a highly specialised medical education as, for example, working in an intensive care unit, but it would be wrong to conclude that this task is not quite demanding and requires little or no training. The demands in this field are different and require other priorities in training. In that respect, there is a deficiency in traditional nursing education which the person-centred concept could fill.

This deficiency is borne out by Erich Grond, a general practitioner and psychiatrist, who for fifteen years had been director of an old people's home in Germany. He defines the nursing process *as a process of problem solving and relating*[4] and criticises 'the lack of qualification' of nursing staff in homes for the elderly: 'More and more vacant positions are filled with auxiliaries, or not filled at all. There is no time for new staff to be properly introduced to the job, the night watch usually is untrained.' And he points to some more nursing deficiencies in homes for aged people: 'Security, order and quiet are given first priority and this often supresses the needs of the inhabitants . . . There is time only for physical care, not for conversation, counselling, or reality-orientation training. If a patient wants to get more attention, he has to pretend to be more helpless or more confused than he really is . . . Inadequate communication, such as one-sided, or in a specialised jargon, or using "we" instead of "you", or talking *about* the patient instead of *with him,* or communication is evasive or given up at all, assuming "anyway he doesn't get it".'[5] All these are points which the person-centred concept explicitly pays attention to. Grond emphasises the importance of the organisational structure and the influence an adequate framework has,

---

3 Käppeli (1991).
4 Grond (1992), p.24.
5 Grond (1992), p. 199ff.

not only on the well-being of the inhabitants but also on the degree of
their confusion. He writes: 'An authoritarian and controlling style of
management is as confusing as a laissez-faire style,' and he blames
house rules which ask for 'absolute quiet from 7 p.m. to 7 a.m.'[6] with
older people who need only about six hours of sleep. Or, 'dinner at 5 p.m.'
and 'breakfast at 8 a.m.' (15 hours without food causes the blood sugar
level to drop and this increases confusion).

The person-centred principle of trusting the potential of growth, can of
course apply to confused or older people. 'A confused person is never
totally confused, never in every aspect, never just progressively, never
invariably, but always has a chance at least to get better.'[7] Adequate
care will considerably contribute to making this possible, as much as
deficiencies in caring cause, or reinforce, confusion. 'Overstressed
nurses get hectic and irritated. Patients are aware of that and get even
more confused. The more stress the carers have, the bigger the
consumption of tranquilisers . . . Carers reinforce what they are actually
afraid of — confusion. They are stressed by their power. A confused
person completely depends on their goodwill.'[8] This way, the goals
Grond sets for caring for confused older persons cannot be achieved:
'Respect human dignity, improve life quality, offer individual support,
according to the history; support autonomy and self-help; foster
relations and social integration.'[9] The following statement repeats
almost exactly the ideas developed earlier in this book: 'It is important
to be empathic and aware of my own input, to see the patient as a
whole person with the abilities he still has and to acknowledge that his
confusion also depends on how I relate to him'[10].

Validation
Validation is a detailed, methodical caring concept for desoriented older
people, developed by the American social worker Naomi Feil[11], based
on 30 years of experience in this area.

Validation, on the one hand, is a development theory for old age, and
on the other hand a method to understand better the often unintelligible
behaviours of older people. Feil describes four stages of disorientation
and offers specific techniques for each stage. She points to the fact
that these stages do not always follow one after the other in sequence,

---

6 Grond (1992), p.201.
7 Grond (1992), p.118.
8 Grond (1992), p.201.
9 Grond (1992), p.288.
10 Grond (1992), p.288.
11 Feil (1982, 1992).

but that a person might change back and forth between the stages. It is important for Feil to know as much as possible about the history of the persons being cared for.

More important than the techniques which, at first sight, appear somehow confusing and hold the danger of using them in a mechanical way, is the attitude on which validation is based. Maria Schmucki[12] writes in her paper: 'When I first read Feil's book, I was startled. Only by studying it more thorouhgly, did I discover that the techniques are just auxiliaries. What is essential is my attitude towards confused aged people, namely to take their feelings and thoughts seriously, to accept and not judge them, and to meet them with empathy, warmth and positive regard.' She experienced the techniques 'not as a restricting corset, but as an opportunity to get in contact with the person and to enter and understand her world.' [13] This is how Maria Schmucki describes working with one client, Mrs M, for ten weeks: 'The more familiar I became with Mrs M, the better I was able to understand and adequately respond to her world. To adequately respond, in my experience, means, above all, to take the feelings and thoughts of a confused aged person seriously, to accept them as *her* feelings and thoughts and to try to understand what she wants to communicate, looking for a bridge into her world in order to understand why she reacts in this and not in another way . . . To adequately respond to the world of a confused older person also means to help her organise her daily life, to find out what she is still able and would like to do, and also to find out what she needs from us, in order to cope with daily life.'[14] Again, in this description we find, in slightly different words, elements of the 'guidelines for daily work' described in Chapter 4 about taking another person seriously and responding to her experiencing, fostering her own way and offering her support for acting independently.

At Haus Schwansen in Rieseby in North Germany, a 42-bed nursing home, the principles of validation are seen as the central issue in caring. In 1994, the staff received an award for their 'exemplary nursing concept'. The aim of this concept is 'to achieve the highest possible life quality for all inhabitants, according to their personal needs and regardless of the degree they are in need of care, or of their stage of dementia . . . Privacy, autonomy, the freedom to choose, dignity, self-actualisation and legal security'[15] are particularly to be granted. Again, the parallels to the person-centred concept are obvious.

12 Schmucki (1994).
13 Schmucki (1994), p.36ff.
14 Schmucki (1994), p.38.
15 Lärm (1995), p.15.

Exemplary too, is the way the concept is integrated in the general setting of the home: 'Each new staff member gets a theoretical introduction and participates in a workshop. The whole staff, by continuous education, deepen their abilities for validating care. The management team gives a living example in meeting inhabitants, staff members, relatives, etc. with a validating attitude.'[16] This corresponds exactly to what in Chapter 7 of this book has been described as the desirable conditions for working in a person-centred way in an institution. If a concept is given this importance and if it gets that much support on the organisational level, the conditions are optimum to work with it in a sensible and constructive way.

16 Lärm (1995), p. 16.

12
A hopeless case?

The following description of individual therapeutic work with a severely mentally disabled, non-verbal woman is an amazing example of a psychotherapeutic process is also possible with people suffering from severe handicaps. Moreover, there is a lot to learn from this example for use in daily life, and from the way it relates to person-centred principles. The German psychologist Barbara Krietemeyer's experience with Laura certainly disproves the widespread notion that for severly mentally disabled people no further development is possible and that the only thing which can be done is to look after them properly.

Laura, thirty-seven years old, is a severely mentally disabled woman. Since her sixth year, she has lived in the same institution. She does not speak, avoids eye contact, is very aggressive towards herself and others and, for her own protection and that of others, has often to be tied down to her bed. She urinates and defecates wherever she is. Her movements are unsteady and sometimes she has difficulty with walking. When anything doesn't suit her, she starts to throw off her clothes, no matter where she is, and it is nearly impossible then to stop her rage. Yet staff members who have worked for many years in this institution remember that things had not always been so bad and that, long ago, Laura even used to roller-skate around the grounds. But in between, Laura's condition got dramatically worse, especially after a particular staff member had left. She now is practically intolerable for the group. She physically attacks her colleagues as well as the carers, throws the dishes around during meals, knocks the chairs down, etc. She has to be isolated most of the time. Supervised by a staff member, she has to eat by herself, after the others have finished their meal. From the room she shared with two room-mates, whom she had attacked time and again, she had to be transferred to a small single room. This was not only to protect the others, but also to avoid having to tie her down so often and to give her a little more space. It is very a small room, though, and she is locked in there almost all day. In order to not completely segregate her from the group, the door has been replaced by bars and a curtain. To offer her some kind of individual care, on four afternoons a week a therapist takes her for a walk.

This was the situation when Barbara Krietemeyer, a new psychologist, began to work in this institution. As the previous therapist was leaving, she was to take over the walks with Laura. To make this transition easier for Laura, they first both together took her for a walk a few times. Laura reacted with jealousy and mistrust towards the new psychologist. As for Barbara, she would have preferred other ways of indivdual care than to take Laura for walks, but this was clearly what she was assigned to. In the staff's opinion, experience had proved clearly that nothing else was possible with Laura.

For the time being, not even this was possible. When Barbara came alone to take her for a walk for the first time, Laura first withdrew to the farthest corner and then immediately attacked the therapist as she tried to enter the room. Barbara tried it time and again; once in a while, with great diffculty, she managed to get Laura dressed and to take her out of the room. But before long, Laura opposed again, either by attacking the therapist or by undressing herself. But most of the time, she wanted neither to get dressed nor to leave the room and vigorously opposed Barbara's attempts to come in. The psychologist, just like the staff, was scared of Laura's attacks. She felt that constantly she had to somehow bring Laura under control and protect herself. Their relations were determined by fear, on both sides. Barbara soon realised that Laura was just as scared of her as she was of Laura. She seemed to experience it as an attack when Barbara entered her (very cramped) room. The therapist decided to no longer press Laura, but for the time being just to sit at the grated door and wait to see what would happen.

During the first two weeks practically nothing happened. Barbara sat at the door, and Laura crawled into her bed and pulled the blankets over her head. However, sitting at this door caused a fundamental change. From this position, Barbara began to perceive Laura differently. She experienced the situation from Laura's point of view. She could not see the others, but heard the noises when they had coffee together, their chatting and laughing, the voice of the carer who sometimes read them a fairy tale; she could hear all this and yet she was excluded. Barbara discovered that Laura's behaviour actually related to what happened outside. For example, she hit her head against the wall when somebody at the table was laughing, and she reacted to voices and to the sound of keys. The psychologist was amazed to realise how much Laura was aware of what was going on with the group and how terrible it must be for her to be excluded from everything, although at the same time she needed the shelter and withdrawal. All at once Barbara no longer just perceived Laura as somebody to be scared of, but as a human being with feelings. This had almost been forgotten by the staff who, not surprisingly, feared her aggression. Barbara was shocked by the terrible emptiness and despair and lack of foundation she sensed in Laura. 'It seemed to me as if she could neither live nor die, and I had the impression that, to some extent, she had given up any hope.'

For six months Barbara Krietemeyer sat at the barred door, for one and a half hours four times a week. What at first had been intended as a stopgap turned out to be a chance to slowly and without fear approach each other a little bit. The bars were a protection for both of them. At that time, Laura was not approachable by language; therefore, in the beginning, Barbara did not attempt to talk to her. Silently and slowly, contact developed. Barbara realised that Laura was reacting to sounds and that she liked to make sounds herself. Sometimes she knocked on her bedstead. Barbara responded by knocking too. Very soon Laura got curious, and once in a while she ventured to put her head out from under the blanket, but immediately withdrew it as soon as Barbara looked at her. Sometimes the therapist played with the marbles she had brought along, letting them jingle or roll over the floor. This seemed to interest Laura. Yet, most of the time, Barbara just sat at the door without doing or saying anything. This appeared to be good for Laura: it gave her space and helped her to express herself in her own way. It was a new experience for Laura that somebody didn't expect anything from her, but just sat there and waited for her to come. After all, the problem was that on the one hand she longed for closeness, but on the other could not stand it. And her aggressions made it hard for the staff to be close, as they constantly had to be defensive. Laura, at that time, could barely cope with anything at all. She could no longer stand the other inmates, and when getting washed or dressed even a minor detail could immediately cause her to withdraw, scream or get aggressive. In daily life there was practically no situation left which could somehow be handled in a positive way.

After two or three weeks, Laura now and then got up, came to the door, squatted down for a moment and went back to her bed. From time to time Barbara tried something different: she sat a little farther away, or closer to the door. The sessions took different courses. Sometimes Laura stayed longer at the door, sometimes she did not come there at all, but remained withdrawn in her corner. It was essential that she could control that herself. Sometimes she turned her bed upside down, took everything out and pulled the mattress towards the door. The therapist saw this as an image of Laura being all churned up inside and also of her wish to be active.

After two or three months Laura's condition got dramatically worse. Now, all her despair broke through. There were sessions when she just cried and hit her head on the wall. Sometimes the therapist almost couldn't endure it: she felt guilty and asked herself if she had to intervene. But at the same time she felt clearly that it was necessary to endure this crisis, with Laura, and get through it. After all, it represented not just a backlash, but also an improvement. Laura was finally able to allow her emotions free rein and to express her desperation. More and more her crying concentrated on the hours with the psychologist, as if Laura would realise that here there was space for her emotions. Once, when it became extremely bad, the therapist spontaneously reflected Laura's feelings: 'It is so bad. You feel so terrible.' This had an immense effect. For the first time Barbara got the impression that Laura actually could grasp words, whereas up to then she had appeared not to be verbally accessible at all. However, and this makes a crucial difference, Barbara had not used words to demand or talk her into something, but to communicate to Laura her empathy with how she felt. Laura obviously got the message. 'To be aware of her situation and to endure that she felt so bad, was the most important thing.' And with this she articulates one of the main principles of the person-centred approach, though at that time she did not consciously work in a person-centred way but used more systemic ideas.

It turned out that, just as with less severely handicapped persons, it was extremely important to be aware of Laura's feelings and selectively to reflect them. For the rest, language still played a minor part. The essential thing was for Barbara to be with Laura's feelings and moods and not to let the contact tear off. 'There was a pre-verbal level intensely present, early experiences, her difficulties and fears, everything she could not articulate, but also her specific way to experience her internal chaos.'

The carer who knew Laura longest confirmed this impression. To her too, it seemed as if Laura had no firm ground any more. In this situation even better conditions in daily life would not have sufficiently supported her. It needed an extra person to take care of her individually. The time she spent at her door allowed the therapist to perceive all the facets of Laura's inner conflict: her wish to be with the others, but at the same time not being able to. Her isolation in daily life — the lack of contact — was just one side of the problem, the other being her inner state to which the unfavourable conditions of her daily life added extra stress. There was no longer any perspective for Laura: nobody believed her capable of anything. Everybody just saw her various behaviour disorders, which concealed everything else. They had all become resigned to the awful situation.

'The fact that I sat there raised hope. "Here is somebody who has not given me up yet," something like that certainly was resonating in Laura's feelings . . . From me too, she had to tolerate impositions. But I could sense very soon that she wanted to take this chance. Despite her terrible despair, to my surprise there was, very early, also a glimpse of hope. Here, finally, there was room for her intense emotions, which usually just were seen as a nuisance. For the first time Laura had space. It is difficult to describe, as hardly anything happened visibly, but there were very intense situations. A dialogue without words had become possible during this half year. Laura also distinctly reacted when I was not totally present sometimes; it was impossible for me to constantly maintain the same intensity of concentration. To realise that there is this subtle level of perception with severely disabled people, and to establish contact, was a fascinating experience. We still have to learn how to use this internal perception. And to proceed in small steps; I was always ten steps ahead, feeling the pressure to do something. Then Laura showed me the limits, and time and again I had to step back.'

There were also dialogues with the marbles or with the tambourine. Barbara rolled marbles through the bars, and Laura rolled them back. Or Barbara beat a rhythm on the tambourine and Laura joined her, or she waited for Barbara to finish and then beat the same rhythm. Distinctly she was able to take up and imitate rhythms. Yet it was not like this all the time, but depended entirely on Laura's condition. Highlights like that were possible, but then again, for longer periods they were absent. There were also times when Barbara Krietemeyer was discouraged and asked herself if what she did made sense at all.

The team had accepted that, for the time being, the therapist did nothing except sit at the door, but it was obvious that they did not like it. Barbara could feel the tension in her back when the group was in the living room. By being there, Barbara in a way got Laura space in the community. At the beginning this was hard for the staff. They were disappointed that it did not work with the walks, because for them it had always been a relief when Laura, for some time, was away from the group. On the other hand, they also felt it as a relief to realise that the psychologist sometimes got stuck too and that she too was scared of Laura. That Barbara could openly admit it helped the team to accept their own helplessness and fears, without feeling guilty or incompetent.

'Though my proceeding initially was intended as a stopgap, just to establish contact, now in retrospect, I am convinced that for Laura it was exactly the right thing. I could not better have thought this up intentionally. *She* gave the signals'. Wholly person-centred, the therapist let herself be guided by these signals, although previously her intentions had been quite different. 'I was glad that Laura, despite her chaos, was so clear after all. I never would have found the way by myself. I

continuously groped along the borders. I often wanted too much. Then
Laura, by her behaviours, set limits. With time I could decode her
behaviour, see it as communication, not as a disorder. This is extremely
difficult with somebody who never talks. Sometimes it is an expression
of feelings, sometimes a statement of will, sometimes a mixture of both.
But she too was changing; with time she found ways to express herself
more clearly. The essential for me was to be aware of and go with what
was important for her. There was nothing I could do but put up with
where she was at the moment. Then she could actually clarify it for
herself. I couldn't do anything for her other than feel what she felt. It
has not even to be reflected, just to feel with can in itself be helpful.
Severely retarded persons sense so much atmospherically. She could
discriminate exactly whether I was empathic or rather distant. I was
surprised how many non-verbal possibilites we have, yet we have to
enter a completely different world where very subtle things play a role.'

For the therapist, it had been essential to free herself from the pressure
to have to do something. Time and again, Laura set limits, and Barbara
had to set back her expectations. 'It was always good for her when I
could tune into what for her was possible at the moment. Yet, the
impulses I gave were important too. There were many things I would
never have found out, had I not from time to time tried out what was
possible. But it was equally important to set back again. It constantly
went back and forth.'

After about six months, Barbara Krietemeyer realised that Laura always
felt visibly better after the one and a half hours she had sat at her door,
even if she had expressed intense sadness, anger or despair. The staff
confirmed that, after the hours with the psychologist, Laura felt better,
and in the evening she was more balanced. The time had come to open
the door and to extend Laura's world bit by bit to the outside. Up to
then this had only been possible for very short actions like going to the
toilet or getting something to drink.

A big step was lying ahead, and the therapist feared that everything
would start all over again. And so it was. Certainly, Laura no longer
attacked Barbara when she entered her room, but the next steps were
extremely difficult. Laura could not stand to be in the group room: she
threw the chairs around, got aggressive again, and Barbara got scared
again, had to protect herself, to control, to hold Laura or lock her in
again — all those elements stressed their relationship. The therapist
had doubts about how this would end if eventually she had to use
force or would hurt Laura. To take Laura outside implied that Barbara
could no longer just relate to her in the role of psychotherapist, but
had to take over also some caring duties, like getting her dressed,

which always was extremely difficult, or having coffee with her. From a therapeutic point of view, this mixing up of roles was far from ideal, and Barbara wished it had been different. But on the other hand, she realised that it could help the staff to recognise that many things were possible in their role too. Situations, which at first she had only seen in terms of caring, she now used as an opportunity to develop other ways to deal with Laura and to change something in her daily life. She lost her fear of entering Laura's room. After all, she still could sit at the door again if it didn't work out. At that time Barbara began to systematically pay attention to where she really had to help Laura and what she was able to do by herself. For example, she held out each piece of clothing for Laura to put them on, one after the other, by herself. Barbara then helped again with closing the buttons. This is what I described earlier in the book as 'offering supports to act independently'.

It was overall a very diffcult interim period: Laura wanted a lot, which then still was not possible for her. She had a strong will, but could not act it out in a satisfying way. She wanted something at once, like going outside, and then wanted something else immediately. Her behaviour was very abrupt and changeable. Her aggression expanded, and at some point it was no longer a solution for the therapist to just lock her up again. Barbara took more risks and tried things out to see how Laura would react. For example, she once anticipated Laura's rage and knocked down all the chairs herself. Laura was flabbergasted, and together they set up the chairs again.

Very soon the therapist also refused to be pulled to and fro. Gently she pushed Laura's hand off her arm and said: 'Please show me what you want. I come with you.' Often it worked. Laura let her go and, by leading the way, showed where she wanted to go. But it also was like a barometer: if Laura needed to hold a hand, Barbara possibly had asked too much. It was interesting though, that one day, Laura herself pushed away the hand of a carer who wanted to take hers, thus showing that she wanted to walk by herself.

When Barbara started to take her outside, Laura first always wanted to go to the (locked) gate and leave the grounds of the institution. The therapist did not hold her back, but went with her to the gate and tried it: the gate was locked. She said, 'The gate is locked,' and invited Laura to try it herself. This did it. Laura could feel that the gate was locked. She turned around and went back. It was crucial that she was stopped by the gate being locked and not by Barbara, and could experience herself that it was locked.

Twenty-five months after she first met Laura, the therapist's work had come close to what she had intended initially. She took Laura regularly to the gym where they could try out things with music, singing and moving. Laura was now able to stay longer with something and decide herself when to set an end to it. Sometimes she by herself reached out for something, like the drum on which she could express her anger and irritation. She had begun to express feelings. The psychologist discovered that Laura usually got aggressive then when she wanted to express something and couldn't. This context made her outbreaks much more understandable. Barbara could now to some degree risk confronting her, on condition that she carefully paid attention to how much Laura could take. This opportunity had not been there previously because there had been no foundation of trust before.

For the staff, Barbara Krietemeyer's efforts served as a model of how things could work differently. They realised that she had other ways to deal with Laura and this opened new possibilites for them too. They plucked up new courage. Laura now could take more, and more things were possible with her. Daily routine, like getting dressed and washed, had become less problematic. There were backlashes too from time to time. Laura reacted badly to a new carer by falling back into old patterns of behaviour. But she could sooner overcome such states and this was a relief, not only for herself but for the staff as well.

Laura has still often to be isolated. Yet she can now more frequently participate in group activities like sitting together after dinner, or little excursions, like a short bus trip or going to the playground. She is now able for a longer time to endure others without becoming aggressive. She takes the dishes to the kitchen by herself, and once in a while she has coffee in the same room with the others — things which before had been impossible. In the evenings her mood is better. She can handle her desires better and she is more clear and self-confident. Overall, Laura's life quality has improved, and for the staff, the stuck situation from which they too had suffered a great deal has begun to move.

It certainly had been a lucky coincidence that this institution had offered the therapist the opportunity to work with Laura so intensely for such a long time, and it goes without saying that such intense individual care is only very rarely possible. Yet this example gives us important clues for everyday work, also in terms of prevention. It shows how helpful and necessary it is, even with severely disabled and non-verbal persons, to never forget that they still have a potential to grow. Moreover, it proves that people like Laura must be taken seriously and that it is actually possible, though not easy, to learn their 'language' if we try to understand their behaviour as a message and not as an imposition.

And something else is made explicit by Barbara Krietemeyers's experience: we can foster other human beings much better if we pick up *their* signals and respond to them with what we have to offer, than if we try to impose on them *our* ideas.

If carers in their daily work do not forget this, if severely disabled persons can sense that carers take them seriously and try to understand them (even if it is not always possible), there is a real chance to prevent things from taking the negative course it had with Laura. Certainly, carers will never have the time, like this therapist, to work so intensely with one person; but what they can learn from her is the attitude towards a so severely disabled person. Barbara Krietemeyer concludes from her experience with Laura that it's the inner attitude of carers that is so important. This attitude works also in daily life and contributes to improving the life quality of people with special needs as well as of their carers, relating to each other in more relaxed and satisfying ways and reducing stress to a tolerable degree.

13
Implications for education and training

The manifold possibilities of integrating the person-centred approach into different professional fields raise the problem of adequate education and training programmes. Can we actually learn to work in a person-centred way? Isn't it an attitude we either do or do not have? Or can we, once we recognise its importance, decide to adopt it? Certainly, the person-centred attitude, based on empathy, positive regard and congruence, is the most important fundamental of this concept. But this attitude cannot just be put on like a uniform. Moreover, there are guidelines and implications about methods resulting from it which we have to know about and transfer into practice.

To listen carefully, to be empathic and able to discern what is going on in ourselves from what we perceive in the other person — all this requires a discipline which can be trained. Empathic imagination certainly is a gift, but it also can be stimulated, encouraged and developed. Exchange between professionals working along person-centred principles in different fields broadens the horizon of our own possibilities. Existing training programmes, workshops and seminars in person-centred counselling, as well as in pre-therapy, may offer different aspects of basic knowledge as well as fostering self-awareness, which in this kind of work is crucial. Learning in this field means first of all becoming more consciously aware of oneself and of others and recognising our own blind spots.

The learning process does not come to an end with the training programmes, but will go on in daily work. Working in a team requires dealing with and coming to terms with each other, settling conflicts, learning from each other and finding constructive solutions. The institution, by its organisation and structures, can contribute much to fostering this process. The guidelines of the concept described in this book provide reference points to orientate around. Consultation and supervision should be made available and will help to recognise problems as well as to find concrete solutions.

Up to now training programmes dealing explicitly with the transfer of person-centred principles into specific working fields are scarce. Here is a demanding challenge for client-centred/person-centred therapists and trainers to take up, in co-operation with professionals from other fields, to try out new avenues and plan person-centred training concepts specially designed for specific professional fields and paying the necessary attention to their respective general settings. Unfortunately, up to now, person-centred circles, including trainers, too often have neglected to consider the realities of different professional fields. The experience described by Petr Ondracek is not an isolated case. The therapeutic situation cannot be transferred to other fields just as it is. Specific ways of person-centred work have to be developed for each professional field, taking its context into account.

Intern training programmes in the institutions are desirable, where person-centred trainers could, together with the staff, develop adequate ways of person-centred work for the specific conditions of this institution. The trainers would contribute their knowledge of the person-centred approach and its applications, and the staff their experience with the involved clients and with the institution.

Mixed groups with participants from different professional backgrounds and work settings can provide fruitful experiences too. Participants mutually benefit from dealing with different professional fields. To be consciously aware of the differences will raise awareness for this aspect of work in general and sharpen perception for their own conditions too. Participants benefit from hints they can give each other from a different, unbiased view, not inhibited by professional blinkers.

As we have seen in Chapter 11, new challenges for education, in terms of integrating humanistic concepts, emerge also in the field of nursing. Particularly in the care of chronically ill and older persons, fundamentals as provided by the person-centred approach are badly needed, in order to develop ways of caring more appropriate to the needs of the patients and at the same time more satisfying for the carers. Traditional basic education in various social professions could substantially and usefully be enriched by person-centred principles.

Besides specific professional knowledge, well-founded training programmes in these fields should:
- convey a deeper understanding for so called 'problematic' persons
- raise awareness for idividual resources
- train capabilities for fostering the development of those resources
- enable carers to recognise their own ideas, impulses and ambitions, and to clearly discriminate them from the needs and concerns of their clients.

These are aspects the person-centred approach attaches main importance to and is highly qualified to convey. A broad field is opening up here for development and pioneer work pointing to the future. Already, since this book has been published in German and in Dutch, some promising steps have been made. In several educational programmes for carers it is required reading. A number of institutions have decided to work with this concept and invite me for intern training and supervsion. I am also involved in person-centred training courses, integrating my concept, as well as elements of pre-therapy, for carers in nursing homes and institutions for people with special needs, organised by Petr Ondracek in the Czech Republic and Germany. There is a real chance, for the concept to slowly and steadily become widespread.

14
Outlook

The concept I have presented in the first chapters of this book arose from the wish to draw general conclusions from my experiences. My point of view has been further confirmed when I discovered, in the examples described in the last three chapters, that substantial elements of this concept turn up again and again in different fields where people work from the basis of person-centred and humanstic principles: there is a need to find ways to work in many different areas, focusing on the person and respecting her integrity. The guidelines I developed in this book apply to various fields and can be implemented in different settings, on condition that these settings are not fundamentally opposed to the person-centred attitude.

The example of the community development in South Africa shows that the person-centred concept is helpful to understand behaviours of people from a completely different cultural background, which at first sight may appear strange. This opens a perspective, not just for South Africa, but also for a better understanding of people from other cultures living in our country. The report from a children's home points to possibilities of approaching educational as well as management tasks with a person-centred attitude. Dion Van Werde's experiences at the psychiatric clinic Saint-Camillus prove how, in many ways, organisation of daily life can contribute to help mentally ill persons to restore or not totally lose their contact with reality. Humanistic approaches in nursing make it clear that the person-centred attitude of nurses is an important factor in the healing process, and that it has a positive effect in relations with geriatric patients, not only on their well-being but also on the degree of their confusion. From Laura's example we can learn that even a severely disabled, non-verbal adult person is able to take considerable steps of growth, if carers succeed in making contact, listen to what this person expresses and let themselves be guided by this.

The guidelines of this person-centred concept are not a rigid prescription. They articulate fundamental principles which have to be implemented in different ways, according to the respective contexts and conditions. To work in a person-centred way requires subtly and precisely considering each individual situation. The question always has to be: What does it mean *in this concrete situation, with this particular person, in these specific conditions* to take seriously, to offer choices, to foster individual ways, etc? Each situation is different, each human being is different, just as the same disease, disorder or handicap has a different effect on each individual. If its principles are taken seriously, person-centred work will never become a rigid routine: it is constantly requiring sensitivity, flexibility and attentive efforts in order to have the desired effects.

Is the potential of the person-centred concept possible at all in an environment where violence and disregard of human dignitiy increasingly become a habit? With this I not only mean the horrific news we get transmitted daily by the media, but also the everyday inconsiderations, violations and injuries of personal integrity happening in close vicinity which can so easily be overlooked: in the school yard, on the bus, in the family, in a crowd, at work, on the road — let alone the intolerance and aggression towards old, weak, disabled or in some other way 'different' human beings.

If we want to work in a person-centred way we also have to see this aspect of reality with open eyes and to not delude ourselves that the world is full of 'nice' people. To trust in constructive forces means we need to be equally aware of destructive tendencies in ourselves too. Only then will we be able to counteract them. Social institutions are no islands of pure selflessness and human kindness, but marked by the same realities and confronted with the same inadequacies as the world around them.

Violence in social institutions is a serious problem which, after not having been talked about for a long time, has only recently begun to be recognised and openly discussed. Stressed staff, inadequate general settings, insufficient training, dissatisfied clients, mutual misunderstanding and lack of funds — these are only a few of many reasons we have to get to grips with, if we want to put things right or, even better, to prevent bad things happening in the first place. To this, the person-centred concept can make a substantial contribution. It is likely to prevent violence and violations of personal integrity — with carers as well as with those taken care of. Violence, in the end, will only produce losers. Whoever disrespects the human dignity of another person, particularly one who is weak and dependent, always violates their own integrity too. Therefore we have to create conditions and ways to work likely to counteract this.

This is not a matter of financial resources, but of priorities. The fact that resources are limited everywhere, undoubtedly makes work in social institutions more difficult. But isn't it, at the same time, a chance to recognise that not every problem is solvable by money and that the most expensive care is not always the best? Shortage of material resources also can be a challenge to employ other resources for the quality of life and satisfaction of all people involved, inhabitants as well as carers.

To work in a person-centred way is not a 'wonder cure' easily solving or getting rid of waiting problems. But it is a constructive and practicable way to confront them in a manner which most importantly respects the integrity and dignity of those concerned. For this, no additional funds are needed, but a change of ideas which everybody involved will benefit from.

References

Feil, N. (1992) Validation: *The Feil Method*, rev. 2nd edn., Cleveland: Feil Productions.

Gogl, A. and Stadelmann-Buser C. (1993) Theoretische Perspektive, in: Käppeli, S. (ed.) *Pflegekonzepte*. Bern: Huber.

Grond E. (1992) Pflege verwirrter alter Menschen. Psychisch Alterskranke und ihre Helfer im menschlichen *Miteinander*. Freiburg i.Br.: Lambertus.

Käppeli, S. (1990) Bio-medizinisches Modell oder Patientenmodell. In: *Krankenpflegeschule aktuell*, 2 (3), Krankenpflegeschule Zürich.

Lärm, M. (1995) Integrative validierende Arbeit, in: *Heilberufe*, 47,3.

Lietaer, G., Rombauts, J. and Van Balen, R. (eds.) (1990) *Client-Cenered and Experiential Psychotherapy in the Nineties*. Leuven: University Press.

Lotz, W., Stahl, B. and Irblich, D. (eds.) (1996) *Wege zur seelischen Gesundheit für Menschen mit geistiger Behinderung: Psychotherapie und Persönlichkeitsentwicklung* . Bern: Huber.

Mearns, D. (1994) *Developing Person-Centred Counselling*, London: Sage.

Mulskers, L. and Van Werde, D. Contact-faciliterend werken binnen een ergotherapeutische setting: een illustratie vanuit residentiële psychosenzorg. (Unpublished script.)

Paterson, J. and Zderad, L. (1976) *Humanistic Nursing.* London: Wiley

Pörtner, M. (1990) Client-Centered Psychotherapy with Mentally Retarded Persons: Catherine and Ruth. In: Lietaer, G., Rombauts, J. and Van Balen, R., (eds.) *Client-Centered and Experiential Psychotherapy in the Nineties*, 659–669, Leuven: University Press.

Pörtner, M. (1994) *Praxis der Gesprächspsychotherapie, Interviews mit Therapeuten,* Stuttgart: Klett Cotta.

Pörtner, M. (1996) *Ernstnehmen, Zutrauen, Verstehen - Personzentrierte Haltung im Umgang mit geistig behinderten und pflegebedürftigen Menschen.* Stuttgart: Klett Cotta). (1999) 2nd edn. *Konzepte der Humanwissenschaften*, Stuttgart: Klett-Cotta.

Pörtner, M. (1996a) Working with the Mentally Handicapped in a Person-Centered Way — is it possible, is it appropriate and what does it mean in practice? In: Hutterer, R., Pawlowsky, G., Schmid, P.F., Stipsits, R. (eds.): *Client-Centered and Experiential Psychotherapy. A Paradigm in Motion,* (513–527) Frankfurt a.M.: Peter Lang, Europäischer Verlag der Wissenschaften.

Pörtner, M. (1998) *Serieus nemen, vertrouwen, begrijpen - cliëntgerichte zorg voor menschen meet en verstandelijke handicap.* Maarssen: Elsevier/De Tijdstroom.

Pörtner, M. (1999) Psychotherapie für Menschen mit geistiger Behinderung. In: *Brennpunkt,* 81/99, 7–13.

Pörtner, M. (2000) Der personzentrierte Ansatz in der Arbeit mit geistig behinderten Menschen. In: Keil, W. and Sturm, G. (eds.) *Der personzentrierte Ansatz in der Psychotherapie. Die vielen Gesichter der klientenzentrierten Psychotherapie.* Wien, New York (Springer, in preparation).

Prouty, G. (1976) Pre-therapy, a method of treating pre-expressive psychotic and retarded patients. In: *Psychotherapy: Theory, Research and Practice,* 13, 290–94.

Prouty, G.(1977) Protosymbolic method: A phenomenological treatment of schizophrenic hallucinations. In: *Journal of Mental Imagery,* 1, (2), 339–4.

Prouty, G. (1983) Hallucinatory contact: A phenomenological treatment of schizophrenics. In: *Journal of Communication Therapy,* 2, 99–103.

Prouty, G. (1986) The pre-symbolic structure and therapeutic transformation of hallucinations. In: M. Wolpin, J. Shorr and L. Kreuger (eds.): *Imagery,* Vol. 4, 99–106, New York: Plenum Press.

Prouty, G. (1990) Pre-therapy: A theoretical evolution in the person-centered/experiential psychotherapy of schizophrenia and retardation. In: Lietaer, G., Rombauts, J. and Van Balen, R. (eds.) *Client-Centered and Experiential Psychotherapy in the Nineties,* 645–58. Leuven: University Press.

Prouty, G. (1991) The pre-symbolic structure and processing of schizophrenic hallucinations: The problematic of an non-process structure. In Lois Fusek (eds.) *New Directions in Client-Centered Therapy: Practice with Difficult Client Populations,* 1–18. Chicago: Chicago Counseling and Psychotherapy Resarch Center.

Prouty, G. (1994) *Theoretical Evolutions in Person-Centered/Experiential Therapy — Applications to Schizophrenic and Retarded Psychoses.* Westport: Praeger.

Prouty, G. and Cronwall, M. (1990) Psychotherapy with a depressed mentally retarded adult: An application of Pre-Therapy. In: A. Dosen and F. Menolascino (eds.) *Depression in Mentally Retarded Children and Adults,* 281–93. Leiden: Logan Publications.

Prouty, G. and Kubiak, M. (1988a) The development of communicative contact with a catatonic schizophrenic. In: *Journal of Communication Therapy,* 4 (1), 13–20.

Prouty, G. (1988b) Pre-Therapy with mentally retarded/psychotic clients. In: *Psychiatric Aspects of Mental Retardation Reviews,* 3 (4), (426–41).

Prouty, G. and Pietrzak, S. (1988) Pre-therapy method applied to persons experiencing hallucinatory images. In: *Person-Centered Review*, 3 (4), 426–41.

Prouty, G., Pörtner, M. and Van Werde, D. (1998) *Prä-Therapie,* Stuttgart: Klett-Cotta. (To be published in 2001 in UK by PCCS Books).

Rogers, C. R. (1942) *Counseling and Psychotherapy,* Boston: Houghton Mifflin.

Rogers, C. R. (1951) *Client-Centered Therapy.* Boston: Houghton Mifflin.

Rogers, C. R. (1957) The Necessary and Sufficient Conditions of Therapeutic Personality Changes, In: *Journal of Consulting Psychology,* 21 (2) 95–103.

Rogers, C. R. (1961) *On becoming a person,* Boston: Houghton Mifflin.

Rogers, C. R. (1969) *Freedom to learn,* Columbus: Carles E. Merrill.

Rogers, C. R. (1970) *On Encounter Groups,* New York, Evanston, London: Harper & Row.

Rogers, C. R. (1977) *On Personal Power,* New York: Delacorte.

Rogers, C. R. (1980) *A Way of Being,* Boston: Houghton Mifflin.

Rogers, C. R. (1982) *Freedom to learn for the 80s,* Boston: Houghton Mifflin.

Schmucki, M. (1994) Validation — ein Weg zur Welt des verwirrten alten Menschen, Kaderschule für die Krankenpflege, Regionalzentrum Winterthur, Höhere Fachausbildung in Krankenpflege, Stufe 1, Kurs Nr. 93038.

Sinason, V. (1992) *Mental Handicap and the Human Condition: New approaches from the Tavistock.* London: Free Association Books.

Van Werde, D. (1990) Die Wiederherstellung des psychologischen Kontaktes bei akuter Psychose — Eine Anwendung von Prouty's Pre-Therapy. *GwG-Zeitschrift,* 21, 78, 42–45.

Van Werde, D. (1993/95) The translation of the contact-paradigm into a ward approach. Written as a documentation for Prouty, G. (1994) and Pörtner M. (1996).

Van Werde, D.(1994) An introduction to client-centred pre-therapy. In: Mearns, D. *Developing Person- Centred Counselling,* London: Sage.

Van Werde, D. (1994a) "Werken aan contact" als leidmotief van de wekelijske afdeilingsvergadering in residentiële psychosenzorg. In: *Tijdschrift voor Psychiatrie,* 8, 571–84.

Van Werde, D. and Van Akoleyen J. (1994) „Verankering" als kernidee van de interieurinrichting in residentiële Psychosenzorg. In: *Tijdschrift Klinische Psychologie,* 24,4, 293–302.

Van Werde, D. and Morton I. (1999) The Relevance of Prouty's Pre-Therapy to Dementia Care. In: Morton, I. *Person-Centred Approaches to Dementia Care,* Oxford: Winslow Press.

First Steps in Counselling 2nd edition

A Students' Companion for Basic Introductory Courses

Pete Sanders
1996 ISBN 1 898059 14 4 200x200 pp138+vi £11.50

This bestselling book is used as the standard course text on hundreds of basic introduction to counselling courses in colleges and independent training institutes throughout the UK. Now in its second edition it comprehensively covers the theory, skills and contextual issues of counselling in the 1990s for all those wanting an introduction to counselling. Each year some 5000 volunteers, social workers, carers, teachers, nurses, community workers, managers, beginning counsellors and their trainers use *First Steps in Counselling* as their starting point for learning.

'This is the second edition of a remarkable book. Its title suggests that it is for beginners only but this is far too modest a claim. . .

The reader is swept into companionship with a trainer and practitioner who knows his subject from top to bottom and who is keenly alert to the whole range of tensions that arise as counselling 'comes of age' in our society. Pete makes no apology for confronting his beginners with some of the harsh realities of what it means to be a counsellor as the twentieth century draws to a close.

At no point, however, does he assume an authoritarian or prescriptive stance. He imparts information — some of it complex and detailed — with lightness of touch . . .

For beginners and their tutors this book will be a resource without price but for the seasoned practitioner, too, it offers much more than an elegant revision course.'
Professor Brian Thorne

'. . . highly accessible with good use of text, diagrams, discussion points and exercises. Sanders' writing style and his creative and appropriate use of poems and popular song lyrics is engaging and adds to the accessible quality and tone of this impressive series*. With suggestions on reading, personal exploration and development, the books parallel — and truly accompany — the learning process.'
Keith Tudor *Person Centred Practice, Vol.5 No.1 1997*

The new introduction to Person-Centred counselling from its origins to current developments in theory and practice

LEARNING AND BEING IN PERSON-CENTRED COUNSELLING
A TEXTBOOK FOR DISCOVERING THEORY AND DEVELOPING PRACTICE

Tony Merry *with additional material by Bob Lusty*

ISBN 1 898059 24 1   156x234 pp approx 180+iv £13.00

THIS BOOK IS a complete rewrite and extended version of the successful *What is Person-Centred Therapy* by Tony Merry and Bob Lusty previously published by the Gale Centre. At almost twice the size of the original, it contains new, up-to-date material and offers in-depth discussion of all aspects of person-centred counselling in theory and practice.

The coverage of the topics is innovative, comprehensive and thorough. Tony Merry is renowned for his straightforward and accessible writing style, making *Learning and Being in Person-Centred Counselling* suitable for a wide variety of readers.

Augmenting the clear presentation, the book is brought to life by many suggestions for exploring and developing person-centred values, qualities, attitudes and skills.

LEARNING AND BEING IN PERSON-CENTRED COUNSELLING is recommended for:
- certificate and diploma in counselling trainees and tutors;
- undergraduate psychology students and lecturers;
- nurses and social workers in training;
- those on vocational and professional helping professions-related courses;
- trainees on integrative, cognitive or psychodynamic courses;
- anyone seeking input on contemporary person-centred theory and practice.

CHAPTERS INCLUDE
- Human nature, actualisation and the development of the person;
- A theory of counselling;
- Developing person-centred values, skills, qualities and attitudes;
- Training issues: client work and personal development;
- Supervision;
- Working and being in groups;
- Resources;

TONY MERRY teaches at the University of East London on postgraduate and undergraduate courses in counselling and counselling psychology. He is author of several books and articles on counselling. He co-founded the British Association for the Person-Centred Approach in 1989 and is currently editor of *Person-Centred Practice* and the *Universities Psychotherapy Association Review.* He has contributed to workshops and other person-centred events in Europe, including several with Carl Rogers in England, Ireland and Hungary in the 1980s.

Bob Lusty *worked closely with Tony Merry at the University of East London for over 20 years. He is now in private practice as a counsellor and supervisor.*

YOU WILL GET A DISCOUNT IF YOU ORDER THIS BOOK BY PHONE.
CALL 01989 770 707 WITH YOUR CREDIT OR DEBIT CARD READY